COPING WITH SCHIZOPHRENIA

THE NATIONAL SCHIZOPHRENIA
FELLOWSHIP

Coping with Schizophrenia

Edited by Dr. Henry R. Rollin
Preface by Lady Wakehurst, D.B.E.

BURNETT BOOKS
in association with ANDRE DEUTSCH

First published 1980 by Burnett Books Limited
in association with André Deutsch Limited
105 Great Russell Street London WC1

Printed in Great Britain by
Lowe & Brydone Printers Limited, Thetford, Norfolk

British Library Cataloguing in Publication Data

Coping with schizophrenia.
  1. Schizophrenia
  I. Rollin, Henry R   II. National Schizophrenia
  Fellowship
  616.8'982   RC514

ISBN 0-233-97245-5

CONTENTS

ACKNOWLEDGEMENTS

WE WOULD LIKE TO acknowledge our indebtedness to the various contributors, each of them an expert in his, or her, particular field, who have so generously contributed papers to this book. We would also like to thank the editor of the *British Medical Journal* for his permission to re-print the paper, 'Schizophrenia', published in that journal on 30 June 1979.

Thanks are due in abundance to our publisher, Farrell Burnett, for her encouragement, understanding and patience.

We are faced with the impossible task of adequately thanking Mrs. Peggy Pyke-Lees, our General Secretary, without whose energy and inspiration there would have been no book — and, in all probability, no National Schizophrenia Fellowship.

Finally, our thanks to the clerical staff of the Fellowship for typing written drafts with such accuracy and at times deciphering the indecipherable.

PREFACE

I AM GLAD to have been asked to write a Preface to this book. My qualifications for so doing are simply my long experience of caring for a much loved relative afflicted with schizophrenia and my need, therefore, to share my problems with others.

One of my sons was gifted, intelligent, active and successful at school and university until, much to our consternation, he started to withdraw into himself and lose his social skills and to blame other people, including myself, for everything that went wrong. The story, indeed, unfolded in the usual tragic pattern.

Doctors seemed unable to help and would not, or could not, explain what was wrong until the 'crisis' came. For those of us who work in the field of mental health, those difficult weeks or months of anxiety, hostility and misunderstanding, and then the recognition of the illness followed by the long search for help and treatment, are all too familiar.

The National Schizophrenia Fellowship was started by a small group of people who felt the need for personal help and involvement and realised the extent and depth of human unhappiness and suffering, the waste of talent, the disruption of family life which mental illness can cause. At the same time, they recognised the lack of facilities in the community to cope with schizophrenia. There are, for example, not enough day centres, sheltered workshops, or hostels − not to mention the indifference of the general public to the plight of the sufferers.

The picture is not all sadness, however. Many patients do recover and return to normal life, although many more are in need of continuous care. To them, what is so important is to feel that somebody cares to help the sufferer to live a meaningful life and not be allowed to slide into apathy and hopelessness. For those who offer care to these sick people comes a deeper understanding and sympathy and a realisation of the saying, 'But for the Grace of God there go I'.

There is obviously a great need for the National Schizophrenia Fellowship. Pioneer work must always be done by people who are prepared to take risks, who have vision, compassion and enthusiasm. Governments can lend support, but can seldom originate.

We are deeply grateful to Burnett Books for publishing this book, thereby bringing information about the National Schizophrenia Fellowship to a far greater audience than would otherwise have been possible. What is presented in plain language are the first-hand experiences of those who suffer and those who care.

Lady Wakehurst, D.B.E.

ONE Introduction and 'A Case of Schizophrenia' *by John Pringle*

SCHIZOPHRENIA — using the term as Eugen Bleuler intended it to be used describing a group of similar but by no means identical illnesses — is a universal mental illness. The disease process has no respect for race, colour, creed, social class, or cultural or intellectual levels. The results, particularly in those cases that prove resistive to treatment and become chronic, can be devastating. Family life can be laid to ruins by the disruption caused by a single schizophrenic member. And yet the cries of distress from these families were like voices in the wilderness: the appeals for help were largely unheeded. In the last decade, however, there has been a decided improvement, an improvement brought about almost fortuitously.

In *The Times* of 9 May 1970, an article entitled 'A Case of Schizophrenia' was published. The author was anonymous. Such was the response from relatives of schizophrenic patients, just as distressed, perplexed and overwhelmed by mixed feelings of guilt and impotence as the author was, that an exploratory committee was formed, the 'Schizophrenia Action Committee'. From this nucleus grew the National Schizophrenia Fellowship.

The identity of the anonymous *Times* correspondent was eventually disclosed. It was John Pringle who thus, more by accident than intent, founded the Fellowship and has continued, since its inception in 1972, to be its President.

His original article has, in effect, become the Fellowship's charter and it is considered right and proper, therefore, to publish it, by courtesy of the Editor of *The Times*, in full and to give it pride of place as the first contribution to this book.

The book has been designed primarily as a guide to the perplexed; to help, that is, the long-suffering relatives of schizophrenic patients understand more about the wretched disease with which they are called upon to cope. It is hoped, too, that there is more than a little in it that will be of interest to the professional – the doctor, the nurse, the social worker – all, indeed, who may at some time be required to lend a hand in the care of the schizophrenic.

Dr. Henry R. Rollin

A Case of Schizophrenia

The word 'schizophrenia' is flung about today with flip facility, bobbing up in films, television scripts, literary criticism, even political articles, mostly as some sort of modish synonym for indecisiveness. But no one who has seen the actual medical condition would ever want to use it except in its correct context.

Schizophrenia is a fragmentation or disintegration of the ego, that central 'I' or 'me' which we all take for granted, unaware of the delicate balance of the elements inside us. According to the severity of the attack, the effects may range from a mild disassociation of personality to a total withdrawal from human contact. Virtually nothing is established about its aetiology or its genetic, environmental or other predisposing factors, so no means exist for either prevention or permanent cure. It may strike at any age or in any walk of life, but there is a distressingly high incidence among young adults, including those of beyond average intelligence. The symptoms may shade into those of many other conditions, so diagnosis can be difficult.

My son succumbed to an alleged 'depression of adolescence' in his second year at Oxbridge, where he had gone with a major open scholarship. He began cutting lectures and tutorials, shutting himself off in his rooms, and avoiding his friends. It did not occur to the college authorities that this behaviour could be due to anything other than idleness. They neither sent him to a doctor nor told us, the parents, but first took away his scholarship – then, as that had no effect, sent him down – with 24 hours' notice to us. They admitted – afterwards – that suicide notes had been found.

A family suddenly faced with this situation has, in my experience, two problems and it is hard to say which is worst. The first is how best to cope with this strange, new member of the household whose moods alternate impossibly between sullen lying on his bed in the dark to wild fits of aggression, with social manners regressed to an almost animal level. The second problem is how to penetrate the obfuscating fog of hospital vagueness and evasiveness to obtain intelligible guidance on the first set of problems.

It is understandable that psychiatrists are chary of affixing a dreaded label too quickly, and in fact it was more than two years, after a round of several hospitals and a disastrous second attempt at Oxbridge, before a positive diagnosis of schizophrenia was made in my son's case. But looking back, were those long months, in which we could get no practical sense out of anybody, really necessary?

On almost any specific point on which advice was desperately needed – should he be persuaded to get up, dress, keep himself clean, encouraged to work or study, or just be left alone, which course was best for him? – we grew used to receiving from the doctors weary platitudes about showing 'patience', or, from the hospital 'welfare' side, surprised counter-questions – 'Didn't you ask the doctor that?' Failures in co-ordination and communication seem to hang about the administrative management of schizophrenia almost like a grim parody of the condition itself.

A personal experience of this kind is inevitably subjectively coloured, but it has persuaded me to look into other cases with which I have no emotional link, and into the general question, and my conclusions are disturbing, particularly about the community provision for the victims of the condition.

Some schizophrenics make a partial recovery. Some stay in hospital for keeps. But thousands more in Britain (the statistics are unreliable) level off like my son at a low level of adaptation, physically fit and normal-looking to a casual outsider, but without application or anything that can be called will-power, and finding most inter-personal relations almost impossibly difficult. Drugs exist which palliate the grosser behavioural disturbances. They make life more tolerable for the sufferer and those around him, but it is hard to hit on a dosage which will not produce a somnolence as inhibiting to normal living as the excess emotion the drugs are designed to suppress or mask. Cases vary, but the very success of the drugs may only make it harder for the outside world to understand that behind the resulting apparent and outward normality the mental fragmentation is still there.

The community problem chronic schizophrenics present is that while not ill enough to be made the subject of a compulsory order, they are incapable of looking after themselves without special guidelines and supervision, notably of either finding a job or, still more, of keeping one. Our son spasmodically looks for the job or occupation which, with one part of his mind, he wants. If he gets it he either does not turn up or he leaves it the same day. He has less sense of money than a child of ten. And each failure with each successive employer, each inability to obtain references, answer letters, keep appointments, repay debts, makes the chance of anything better progressively more remote.

Schizophrenics tend to leave behind them a trail of people who righteously, or despairingly, feel they have 'done as much as we can' and it should be somebody else's turn. I have quite a collection of sympathetic letters 'hoping your son's condition will soon improve' while regretfully saying 'no' to some specific request.

Such reactions are all too intelligible, bearing in mind the maddening vagaries of schizophrenics and the difficulty of fitting them into any normal pattern of living. They excite none of the sympathy which surrounds other classes of the disabled. Even close relatives, let alone official bodies or employers, find it not easy always to choke back the feeling that there is something *morally* culpable about people apparently fit and rational who fling up work without excuse, and whose hands, as the years go by, increasingly close over any small gift of money with what looks like complacency but is in reality only a sad acceptance of their inadequacy.

As regards their ultimate disposal, if one must use the callous term, they present a problem which, it seems to me, the community and the authorities just are not facing. The priority matter is clearly rehabilitation wherever this is possible: a dual task of resocialising to enable them at least to scrape by in company with normal people, and simultaneously fitting them to do some simple job, possibly very much part-time, but at least permitting them to live independently, if only at a modest subsistence level. Central or local provision for retraining geared to the needs of schizophrenics (or for that matter, former mental patients in general) is virtually non-existent.

The Industrial Rehabilitation Units set up by the old Ministry of Labour are primarily intended for physically injured or handicapped manual workers. They are too few and scattered in view of travelling difficulties, but, that apart, they concentrate on industrial retraining whereas many schizophrenics are only fit for routine clerical or similar work and are often so manually clumsy that to let them anywhere near lathes or power tools is inviting trouble. Worse still, the Industrial Rehabilitation Units naturally expect punctuality and the keeping of regular hours, both of them major hurdles to the average schizophrenic who after an initial failure seldom goes back.

To meet the resocialising part of the rehabilitation process a recent Act laid on local authorities the obligation to establish hostels to act as 'halfway houses' for mental patients between their discharge from hospital and the hoped-for resumption by them of normal living. The aim, the provision of an interim sheltered environment, was admirable, but only a handful of local authorities have in fact done anything. And of those who have, some have interpreted their task in a grudging, obscurantist spirit.

The so-called halfway house set up by a wealthy county close to London is run on strict disciplinarian lines. New arrivals have it rubbed into them that their first duty is to get a job and get out. Use of the premises is forbidden during the day, almost as though intended to make the inmates feel rejected and walk the streets aimlessly, a favourite schizophrenic way of passing the time.

Pressure on schizophrenics to obtain occupation may be right, for their own sakes and to prevent deterioration, but hectoring is counter-productive and the ambience which brings out their best is more that of an oversized family than an institution. For this reason the most successful halfway houses are those set up by such admirable voluntary bodies as the Richmond Fellowship whose staff must by now have as much experience of schizophrenic rehabilitation as anyone in the country. But there are tragically few of them.

When all is done a hard core will remain, possibly running well into five figures for the United Kingdom, who will never be capable of fending completely for themselves. No social provision exists for them, so their future is bleak. As parents die off and other relatives find it impossible to cope, the inevitable trend is for them to drift downwards to the welfare state's bottomest sump. A recent 'Panorama' item gave a grim but accurate account of what is already happening to many: discharged from hospital to nobody and nowhere, feebly attempting casual work, neglecting their medication, failing even to collect their 'public assistance'; the will-less slide to the doss house or sleeping rough along with the meths drinkers and drug addicts, involvement with police and prison, or, if lucky, back to hospital and starting the process over again.

Mental hospitals or institutions for mental defectives are totally inappropriate for giving shelter to chronic schizophrenics, but where else can they go? What is wanted are small residential settlements where their simple basic needs, including protection from impossible stress, can be provided in a mutually supportive environment. Such homes would be far cheaper than a corresponding occupancy of places in mental hospitals with their high medical and other overheads and where any attempt at normal living, to which they pathetically cling, is impossible.

Many of the necessary jobs could be done by the residents themselves; schizophrenics will often work well enough in their own fashion if someone they like will tactfully 'organise' them and is tolerant of their vagaries. There would also be scope for sympathetic local employers, not expecting too much, to give them a try. Such small communities would fill a gap in our social provision, avoid the friction and waste inherent in the present administrative neglect, and offer thousands in the hard core their best chance of happiness.

But the whole administrative set-up for dealing with this category of the disabled needs pulling together. The mentally crippled can almost be relied on to hurl themselves through any safety net devised to catch the ordinary disabled but this should be foreseen at the planning stage. Unaided, they cannot be expected to cope with the bewildering maze of authorities which impinge upon their lives: out-patient departments, almoners, departments of employment and social security, inland revenue, hostels, local authorities, Industrial Rehabilitation Units, each with its demands for documents, replying to letters, giving precise answers to incomprehensible questions – and none appearing to be in touch with the others.

The ideal would be for some one authority to be given a co-ordinating role and designated as that to which schizophrenics can turn in all matters affecting them. If this involves registering them that too should be considered. The scandalous fragmentation of responsibility between local authorities and the hospital service – the one wanting schizophrenics off the rates even at the cost of their occupying expensive NHS beds, the other responsible solely for the medical aspects and unconcerned with any comprehensive after-care – should be ended. A unified national policy is needed.

TWO A Note on the Significance and Evolution of the Term Schizophrenia
by Henry R. Rollin

BEFORE PSYCHIATRY became an acknowledged speciality in its own right, physicians had a makeshift classification of diseases of the mind, diseases which have, of course, been in evidence and described since the beginning of recorded history. A case in point is delirium. Delirium is a state of transient madness. It can be caused by the invasion of the body by pathological organisms, as in pneumonia; by poisoning with alcohol or other noxious substances, and particularly in this day and age, hallucinogenic drugs (the amphetamines, lysergic acid and the opiates, for example). All these forms of delirium, or cerebral excitement, were differentiated in bygone days from mania, a psychiatric condition characterised by overactivity of mind and movement, by the absence of fever – 'excitement without fever' was indeed the one-time definition of this particular mental illness. At the other end of the affective spectrum, depression, commonly manifested as the obverse phase of mania in the condition of manic-depressive psychosis, has always been well recognised. However, as with mania, depression embraced a very heterogeneous group of mental illnesses. For the rest, psychiatric maladies had been loosely grouped into what was termed catalepsy and ecstasy, hysteria and hypochondriasis, and those maladies associated with damage to the substance of the brain. The term 'schizophrenia' neither appeared in the nomenclature, nor was it recognised as a clinical entity, until the present century.

At the very end of the nineteenth century however, there was a brave attempt by German psychiatrists to chart the wasteland of psychiatric diagnosis. In 1898 Dr. Emil Kraepelin coined the term 'dementia praecox' – an unhappy choice as it turned out – in an attempt to separate the mental illnesses that lead inexorably to disintegration of the personality from affective disorders – manic-depressive phychosis, for example – which do not. In 1911, Dr. Eugene Bleuler went further and spoke of 'the group of schizophrenias' (the very first time the term was used) which included Kraepelin's dementia praecox, but added similar, if not identical, illnesses in which true dementia — an irreversible deterioration in mental ability — did not necessarily take place.

It is important at this point to add, even parenthetically, that there is a growing misuse of the term schizophrenia by the laity. The condition is often described as having a 'split mind' which is a total misconception. There are cases described in the psychiatric literature, and others that have been used as the basis of the plot of novels as in, for instance, *The Three Faces of Eve* in which a splitting of the mind, or personality, is portrayed. Such cases are not examples of schizophrenia, but of hysterical dissociation, a condition in which the mind loses its cohesion and allows parts of it to act autonomously: two, or even more, 'personalities' may co-exist.

Even so, the definition of mental illnesses by professional psychiatrists remains unsatisfactory. This is particularly so of 'schizophrenia' which, despite Bleuler's teaching, has once again come to be regarded as a single disease entity. What is even more disconcerting is that the interpretation of 'schizophrenia' varies not only from country to country, but from one area of the same country to another. A particular professor of psychiatry in a particular university may impose his own idiosyncratic views on diagnosis on his students which may be at variance with those of other professors at other universities. This failure of diagnostic precision is a matter of grave concern. It creates a serious communication barrier between psychiatrists, and as a result, impedes the possible development of a specific form of treatment.

However, there is at the present moment a concentrated and continuing effort to bring order into chaos both nationally and internationally. For example, there are the U.S.–U.K. Diagnosis Project based at the Maudsley Hospital, London; the World Health Organization International Pilot Study of Schizophrenia; and the Medical Research Council Social Psychiatry Unit of which Professor Wing is the Director.

Undoubtedly, some progress is being made, but there is a long way to go. It can only be hoped that in the not too distant future psychiatrist will be able to talk to psychiatrist and understand what each other means when one or the other uses the term 'schizophrenia'.

THREE Schizophrenia at Home
by Professor John Wing and Clare Greer

THIS CHAPTER'S prime importance lies in the fact that it, to quote a phrase from the introduction, is 'concerned to provide a factual description of the impact of schizophrenia on relatives and of how the consequent difficulties are coped with. ...' The concern is, as will be seen, not with hypothetical musings, but with the cold, hard, and sometimes cruel, facts which face those having to live with someone near and dear to them whose mental illness has reduced him to a caricature of what he was, and would have continued to be, had he not fallen victim to schizophrenia.

The chapter in its original form was published in 1974. It was based on interviews with 50 relatives belonging to the National Schizophrenia Fellowship, residing in three geographical areas (London, the Midlands and the North) and 30 relatives of schizophrenic patients living in one defined area of inner London (Camberwell) by way of comparison. However, it is considered that the differences between the two groups, interesting as they may be, are largely of academic importance.

For our present purposes it is considered sufficient to aggregate the data emerging from the interviews with the two groups of relatives.

Dr. Henry R. Rollin

Introduction

This report deals with the problems experienced by people who live with, or feel responsible for, a relative who has been diagnosed as suffering from 'schizophrenia' or from one of the conditions loosely grouped together under the label of 'schizophrenia'. It is not, therefore, primarily a clinical document nor does it focus on the problems of the affected individuals themselves, except in so far as these are seen through the eyes of relatives. We have chiefly been concerned to provide a factual description of the impact of schizophrenia on relatives and of how the consequent difficulties are coped with, the object being to provide a systematic basis on which to suggest how management and services might be improved.

It has frequently been noted that relatives tend to understate their problems. There are many reasons for this. For example, the severity of the disorder fluctuates. If things are all right at the time the interviewer calls, the course of previous events appears more tolerable and crises which were agonising at the time tend to lose some of their urgency. Then the questions asked by professional interviewers are often not couched in such a way that intimate problems, such as the sex life of a married couple, can easily be discussed. Next, the significance of questions about what extra services might be provided may not be appreciated by relatives who have no experience of what a really good social and medical service is like. Above all, many relatives who live with disabled people tend to adjust their level of expectation so that, after a period of years, they no longer react according to earlier hopes and ideals for their own personal life and perhaps have even forgotten what they were. Finally, many relatives, particularly mothers, find that a sense of duty or common humanity makes them willing to undergo considerable distress, discomfort or embarrassment without complaint.

The opportunity to talk to a group of relatives who have banded themselves into a charitable fellowship in order to try to promote the welfare of all those affected, directly or indirectly, by schizophrenia, is therefore a significant one. The major advantage offered is that the more articulate and thoughtful relatives will be able to speak for the rest. This carries a potential disadvantage, in so far as such a self-selected group is not representative, but a parallel survey of a randomly selected group of relatives can be used to put the results into perspective.

The National Context

Schizophrenia affects about one person in a hundred, at some time during the course of a lifetime. In the 1930s, before the rediscovery of methods of benign social care and before the introduction of any of the modern pharmacological treatments, the chance that someone with this diagnosis, who was admitted to a mental hospital for the first time, would be discharged within a period of two years, was only one in three. Once resident for as long as two years, the chance of ever being discharged at all became minimal. There was, of course, a small proportion, even in those days, who recovered, but the overall outlook was gloomy. Nowadays the picture is quite different, with the period of residence in hospital being cut to a matter of weeks or months and only a very small proportion, less than ten per cent, staying even as long as a year.

This trend is illustrated by the decline in the numbers of occupied beds in mental hospitals, from its maximum of 344 per 100,000 population in 1954 to 225 per 100,000 at the end of 1971. This decline is due in large part to the fact that schizophrenic patients now rarely become long-stay residents.

The national plan envisages that the decline will continue, so much so that, eventually, much smaller local psychiatric units in general hospitals will be able to deal with the needs for short-term

Table 1
Some characteristics of the relatives

Characteristic		Total (N = 80)
Interview with:	Parent(s)	49
	Spouse	11
	Sibling	12
	Other kin	8
Patient lives with:	Parent(s)	26
	Spouse	16
	Other kin	9
Patient lives in:	Flat, digs	13
	Hospital	16
Children under 14 in same household with patient		15
No children in household with patient		65
Relative has:	non-manual work	48
	skilled manual	16
	semi or unskilled	6
Relative is:	old-age pensioner	8
	unemployed	2

treatment while the protective functions of the mental hospitals can be taken over by a variety of social agencies set up by local authorities and voluntary bodies. At the moment, therefore, we are in a transitional period. On the one hand, the mental hospitals are running down but are still solidly in existence. On the other hand, the projected alternatives, both medical and social, are nowhere provided on a scale which could possibly be regarded as adequate.

This is a good time to carry out a survey of relatives' problems, since relatives can observe the gaps and deficiencies which the new model service will have to fill, and recommendations based on their experiences stand some chance of influencing the future pattern of development.

One other feature of the current scene must be mentioned and that is the so-called 'anti-psychiatry' campaign. This takes several quite different forms but common to all of them is an

Table 2
Some characteristics of the patients

Characteristic		Total (N = 80)
Age:	18–30	40
	31–50	26
	51–60	14
Sex:	Female	23
	Male	57
Married and living with spouse		16
Divorced or separated		8
Unmarried		55
Widowed		1
First admission:	less than five years ago	28
	6–15 years	39
	16+ years	11
	not known/not applicable	2
Never admitted to hospital		1
One admission only		14
Several admissions		34
Many admissions		31
Any admission lasting more than 1 year		27
No admission lasted 1 year		53

assumption that schizophrenia is a condition created by those who label it. Parents, doctors and members of the helping professions are stigmatised as people who, instead of trying, however inadequately, to cope with the effects of a condition which can sometimes be crippling, are in fact responsible for it. The essence of this theory is a denial of handicap and an imputation of guilt to relatives. This is not, of course, a new experience for relatives, but taken in conjunction with the trend towards 'community care', which sometimes means little more than that the responsibility is transferred from hospital to home, the pressures on relatives are likely to be more immediate and direct.

It should be remembered, throughout, that the main purpose of both surveys was to be sure that the main types of problems were represented and described. It was not intended to give a precise estimate of how often these problems occur throughout the country, although some very tentative guesses can be made.

Behaviour

The Main Symptoms of Schizophrenia

Schizophrenia is chiefly recognised because of certain unusual features of thought, behaviour and mood. Most striking perhaps, and most puzzling to inexperienced people, are the disorders of thought, which result in delusions, hallucinations and abnormalities of speech. The patient may hold demonstrably false ideas with unshakeable conviction, may hear voices which no-one else can hear and may speak incomprehensibly or use words or expressions which other people do not understand. The behavioural disturbances may be directly linked to the thought disorder, as when patients act upon a delusional belief, or in response to orders from hallucinatory voices. They may talk out loud to themselves or behave in an unpredictable or odd manner which demonstrates their difficulty in thinking straight. They may be overactive and even, rarely, violent. Another very common behavioural abnormality, however, can be summarised under the heading of 'social withdrawal'. The patient becomes slow, underactive, reticent, lacking in energy or initiative, self-neglectful and seemingly self-absorbed. The abnormalities of mood include exaltation, depression, irritability and anxiety. Most common, however, particularly when social withdrawal is present, is an appearance of flattening of mood. The patient's facial expression is wooden, he does not use gesture or posture or variation in tone of voice to help verbal communication and he tends to react as though his emotions were blunted. He may be amused by situations which other people would find sad.

All these symptoms may be present singly, or in combination, one following another, and they may range in severity from barely detectable by an expert to extremely and publicly obvious. What we shall try to do in this chapter is not so much describe the symptoms, since that has been ably done many times before, but to see them through the eyes of relatives.

In Table 3, 17 characteristics of behaviour, thought or mood are shown in order of the frequency in which they occurred to a very marked or somewhat marked degree in the total group of 80 patients. The commonest were undoubtedly those traits

Table 3

Behavioural characteristics of patients in rank order of frequency

Characteristic	Total (N = 80)	%
1. Social withdrawal	59	74
2. Underactivity	45	56
3. Lack of conversation	43	54
4. Few leisure interests	40	50
5. Slowness	38	48
6. Overactivity	33	41
7. Odd ideas	27	34
8. Depression	27	34
9. Odd behaviour	27	34
10. Neglect of appearance	24	30
11. Odd postures and movements	20	25
12. Threats or violence	18	23
13. Poor mealtime behaviour	10	13
14. Socially embarrassing behaviour	6	8
15. Sexually unusual behaviour	6	8
16. Suicidal attempts	3	4
17. Incontinence	3	4

N.B. Each of these items was rated as occurring to a very, rather, or slightly marked extent or not at all. The numbers given here refer to those rated as occurring to a very marked or rather marked extent.

associated with social withdrawal. These will therefore be described first. Although, when severe, these characteristics may be very difficult to live with, the other ones, which are less common, are more likely to be socially embarrassing and to give rise to a great deal of intolerance if they occur in public. They will be described in a separate section.

Withdrawal from Social Contact

The most withdrawn patients tried to avoid all contact with other people; one young man would reach for his cigarettes and make a dash for his room as soon as the doorbell rang. Another young man was often sent to do some shopping by his parents in order to get him out of the house for a while. He usually returned home very quickly and often with the wrong goods. 'He just grabs whatever is nearest to hand in the shop so that he can dash out as quickly as possible'. Some patients were terrified of leaving the house. One informant said she could never persuade her brother to walk any distance because he had to feel he could get back to the house quickly. Some patients were withdrawn in this way only during an acute attack of the illness and were otherwise quite sociable and able to mix normally. Such a person might cut friends dead in the street, which would seem very odd to them if he was usually friendly and outgoing.

There were many patients who liked other people around but did not like to interact with them directly. 'He likes to go to family parties – he enjoys them even though he just stands on his own and doesn't speak to anyone'. One lady said she had been surprised to hear from a friend that her nephew suffering from the disease liked to come and visit her. 'I would never have guessed it because when he comes he just sits in a chair and says absolutely nothing'. Other patients would have liked more contact with people but lacked the confidence to cope with social situations. Often this was because they felt self-conscious, and thought that everybody was looking and laughing at them. Such patients had often made attempts to attend social functions but had had to leave, unable to bear the situation. They then felt rejected and bitter if relatives went without them on the next occasion.

One middle-aged lady refused to go down to the local pub on a Friday night with her sisters. Before her illness they had always gone together and used to play the piano or sing there and thoroughly enjoyed themselves. This lady said she could not go now, 'because I'm sure everyone thinks I look shabby'. Her sisters had tried hard to persuade her this was not so, but to no avail, so now they went without her. She was, however, rather hurt by this and said, 'It makes me feel I'm not wanted'.

Some patients would make remarks which offended people: 'He's so abrupt and blunt, people just don't want to know him'. These patients did not understand the function of the 'small talk' which keeps much social interaction going. Instead, they may ask direct and embarrassing questions. For example, 'A young lady came to visit us the other day, and my daughter started asking her if she had a boyfriend and all sorts of personal questions'. Sometimes if a patient like this has young brothers or sisters living at home, it can be very embarrassing for them when they have their friends round. One patient would 'collar his brother's friend as soon as he comes in the door, and talk at him non-stop till someone comes and rescues him'. Some relatives were concerned about a patient's naivety in his attitude to people. Such patients were described as 'much too trusting' and 'easy to con'. Often relatives felt very worried if a patient like this began to mix with people who were liable to take advantage of him.

Many relatives had tried to help patients with their problems in mixing socially. Some had had considerable success by encouraging the patient to join some club or activity which had worked out well. Several, however, after many years' experience of coping with the illness, said they had learned the hard way that it was no good imposing their own aspirations on the patient. They had had to accept that he would never want the kind of social relationships that they would like him to want.

A common problem was that the patient was quite unable to occupy himself during the day and had little interest in anything, so that his life was a long series of empty hours stretching between breakfast and bedtime. Some idea of how many hours were spent completely unoccupied was gained by asking relatives to describe how the patient usually spent the day.

Information was available for 42 patients altogether; 17 of these (41%) seemed to be very inert. One literally did nothing at all. The other 16 spent 2–5 hours a day doing absolutely nothing. Altogether two-thirds of all the 80 patients were reported as being markedly or somewhat underactive. However, even those who had some activity tended to adopt some ritual way of spending the time, for example, by brewing tea continuously or chain-smoking. Someone who went out to work but spent most of his evenings and weekends lying on his bed would also be classed as 'rather underactive'. One relative explained graphically that, 'in the evenings you go into the sitting-room and it's in darkness. You turn on the light, and there he is, just sitting there, staring in front of him'. Some relatives used the word 'uncanny' to describe this kind of behaviour. One mother said her son spent most of his time closeted in his room, only coming out at night when everyone was in bed. Usually he was talking to himself and moving about but every few weeks there would be complete silence for a few days. 'After that has been going on for a day or two, I sometimes wonder whether he is dead'.

Many relatives, when they were asked about underactivity, mentioned another problem which worried them; that of excessive sleeping. Some patients, for example, might spend the whole of Saturday 'in a deep, coma-like sleep' (as one mother put it). Relatives wondered if this kind of sleeping was harmful, and whether it was an indication that the patient's medication was too strong for him. One mother said she was always afraid that one day she would not be able to rouse her son from his very deep sleep.

Relatives had various theories to explain the periods of total inactivity and the long hours spent in bed. Many felt that it was because ordinary everyday living and contact with people was simply an unbearable effort to the individual suffering from schizophrenia; he had to withdraw and 'recharge' himself frequently. As one mother put it, 'He just can't bear *people* — even to be in the same room as another person'. One patient had himself explained that he had to have the time lying on his bed, because he was 'all fizzing up inside'. Some relatives feared that if they allowed too much underactivity, the patient would get worse, and therefore insisted that the patient should perform certain household tasks, even though they had to stay in the room with him to make sure he did them and even though the pace at which he worked was often painfully slow. Others decided this kind of thing was too exhausting. 'I'd sooner not ask him to wash up', one said, 'because it only means he uses cold water or forgets to use any washing-up liquid, or leaves half the food on the plates'. Some people tried to keep the patients active by keeping them entertained as much as possible – taking them out in the car, for walks, etc. But this was usually very draining emotionally.

Sometimes a relative would give a patient money to go to a cafe for lunch or tea, in order to get him out of the house for a while at least. One relative said, 'I know it isn't fair, because he can't help it, but it's so annoying when you've got lots of housework to do, and there he is, a fine healthy-looking young man, and he just *sits* there doing absolutely nothing'. Even more irritating was the habit some had, of following their mothers from room to room as they went about their household tasks.

Many relatives had tried to encourage a patient in some hobby or interest, but often after a brief enthusiasm, the patient would lose all interest. 'He can't concentrate on anything – not books, T.V., or anything. He's always changing his interests. It's something different every week'. Often patients seemed to find concentration very difficult. For example, a highly intelligent young man, who had previously had academic interests, now found it impossible to read more than a few pages of a book at a time. On the other hand, a few relatives had successfully managed to interest a patient in some pursuit. Sports clubs, ballroom dancing classes, poetry groups, were examples. Usually it entailed one of the relatives going with the patient to the activity at first, but later he was confident enough to go on his own.

The patients' lack of conversation was another very frequent complaint. A few patients hardly spoke at all, like the young man who came home from hospital each weekend, and who 'quite often doesn't speak a word the whole weekend, then when it's time to go back you ask him, "have you enjoyed your weekend?" and he just says "No" '. Sometimes, however, it turned out that a patient was taking more interest in a conversation than he appeared to be. One young man generally sat in silence, or muttering to himself, while his parents were conversing about family matters. Later, however, they learnt that he had quite often spoken to a nurse at the hospital about such topics of conversation at home, and had clearly been taking in what was said despite all appearances to the contrary. Several relatives mentioned that patients seemed to be more taciturn with them than with outsiders. They would often make an effort to speak a little to visitors who called, though they would not do so with the family.

Most patients did carry on some sort of conversation from time to time but used few words and tended to lapse into silence rather frequently. There were periods when they seemed not to hear relatives speaking to them, and did not answer questions. Or else they might answer, but only in monosyllables. One mother said she had asked her very taciturn son, 'I do wish you would *talk* a bit more,' to which her son replied, 'Well, what is there to talk about?'.

Relatives had various ideas about the reasons for this lack of communication. Some wondered if the patient was silent because he was brooding over something which was depressing him; they associated silence with 'moodiness' and unhappiness. Others felt the silence was protective – that the patient needed it, just as he needed periods of total inactivity – 'He doesn't need to talk because he wants to protect his inner life from intrusion'. Others felt that talking was exhausting for the patient 'because he lives in his own private world, and it's such an *effort* for him to bring himself into the real world'. Occasionally, the patient's silence was markedly hostile in nature. One, for example, would have times when he would 'refuse to sit near you, would look at you like something the cat brought in, and refuse to speak to you'. When this happened relatives could become very anxious and guilty, wondering what they had done to provoke so much silent hatred.

A patient's silence was much more of a problem for the relative who depended a lot upon him for company. Husbands and wives, for example, normally expect a good deal of companionship from each other. When the spouse suffering from schizophrenia cannot offer this, the lack of two-way communication leads to resentment and frustration for the other partner. For different reasons, the same thing often applied to a rather isolated relative, living alone with the patient. As one elderly lady said, 'It's just the way he never says anything to you, and doesn't seem to hear what you say to him that gets me down. I'd rather have him living here than be on my own, but I do wish he had more conversation'.

Slowness was another common problem. Some patients were slow in their movements all the time. Others only showed periods of slowness and moved normally the rest of the time. One mother described how she would watch her daughter walking up the road very slowly and stopping still for a while every few yards. Others mentioned how long a patient would take over the household tasks, doing them in a very slow, roundabout way, for instance, 'vacuums the floor doing a little square at a time, very slowly and stopping every few minutes in a fixed sort of posture'. Slowness was mentioned as a particular problem for patients who worked. It could be one of the reasons they had problems in their jobs, being unable to keep up the expected pace. This was also true of some of the housewives, who found that their work built up until they felt overwhelmed by it, because they could not get through it quickly enough.

Some relatives felt that a patient was clumsy and uncoordinated rather than slow; inclined to knock things over, break cups when drying them up, etc. Many relatives found a patient's constant slowness annoying. 'Sometimes I feel like saying, "Oh! For goodness sake do get *on* can't you?" ', one commented, adding guiltily, 'I know I shouldn't, I know she can't help it'. Her feelings of frustration were shared by many relatives.

Some patients would completely neglect certain aspects of hygiene, refusing to clean their teeth for example, or refusing to have a bath. On the other hand the same patient could be extremely fussy about something else, such as washing his hands every five minutes, or continually combing and re-combing his hair. Relatives sometimes said that a patient's dishevelled or positively bizarre appearance would cause people to turn and look at him in the street. This tended to reinforce any ideas he might have about people laughing at him and talking about him. One patient complained about this. The relative pointed out that people were staring because he looked dirty and unshaven, but he became extremely angry at this.

Many relatives found that a direct approach to this problem did not work. For example, a patient might be more likely to wear a clean set of clothes if these were left hanging casually over a chair, than if they were actually offered to him. However, in other instances a straightforward request was effective. Some relatives simply reminded the patient to wash every morning, and told him to change if his clothes were dirty, and he accepted this as part of normal daily routine.

Problems at mealtimes probably had a lot to do with the patients' general inability to cope with social situations. Indeed some simply avoided the whole problem by refusing to eat with the family, and insisting on having all meals alone in their bedroom. Others might gobble a meal down without much regard for table manners so as to escape as quickly as possible. One relative said, 'I used to get upset at the way he'd pile a load of food on his fork and shovel it into his mouth. But I couldn't tell you if he still does it because I've got into the habit of never looking at him now.' Sometimes patients were suspicious about food and would sniff it dubiously or push it away disgustedly. Some relatives felt this was done intentionally to be annoying. Patients also had food fads from time to time, and might exist for periods on very odd diets.

Relatives were asked about incontinence, but as it turned out, the number of cases where this was a problem was negligible. Three subjects were occasionally incontinent of urine but in only one of these cases did this constitute a fairly serious problem.

Depression and Suicidal Ideas

It was not always easy to obtain information about depression and relatives' views were not always as informed as they were when other aspects of behaviour or mood were being described. Many, for example, interpreted reticence and social withdrawal as evidence of a depressed mood without any more direct indication of depression being present. A rating was not made unless further evidence was available; for example, if the patient talked about the worthlessness and pointlessness of life, or cried, or actually looked depressed. About one third of the group had fairly recently been depressed, according to these criteria.

Some patients, for example, had episodes during which they became morose and felt that life was not worth living. Quite often, this seemed to be due to a comparison made by the patient between himself and his brothers and sisters who were following a successful career, getting married, having children, and in general leading ordinary 'normal' lives. One patient, for example, could not hold down a job and became tearful and distressed when his younger brother, still at school, took a holiday job. Another said, 'I'd rather be a cripple than be like I am. I'm no use to anyone'. Others spoke of not being able to face the years ahead of them; wishing they could have an accident, and die. In some cases, relatives noticed that the depression came in cycles and could more or less be predicted. Sometimes a patient would always be depressed at a certain time of day. If he worked, this might well be in the evening when he came home.

One mother described how the patient, a young man in his twenties, had regular 'fits of depression' about every six weeks. He would sit in the chair, cry, dribble and talk incoherently about how unhappy he was. His mother dealt with this by talking sympathetically to him, putting him to bed, and wiping his face with a flannel to calm him down. He would then go to sleep and would be all right the next day. Because she knew how to cope with these moods and more or less knew when to expect them, his mother was not unduly worried about them.

One lady, the wife of a patient, described how her husband had lately been depressed about his work. He came home every night and went straight upstairs where he lay on his bed all evening. This annoyed his wife, as she worked all day too. They also had four children (aged eleven to fourteen) and the patient's wife felt they should see their father in the evenings. However, if she shouted up to her husband to come downstairs, he would curse and swear at her, saying 'Can't you understand that I'm full up to here with work?'

Some mention of suicide was not uncommon. About one quarter of all the patients had said something about it during the previous year. Sixteen had actually made an attempt at some earlier time and three had made serious suicide attempts during the year. (See Table 4). Even if the attempt had been a long time ago, however, relatives would still feel anxiety about it. As one put it, 'Because she's done it once, it is always at the back of your mind that she might do it again'. Sometimes patients threatened suicide when angry and relatives did not know how seriously to take this. More frightening were the occasions when a patient tried to kill himself 'out of the blue', and without any immediately obvious external reason. One, for example, seemed quite cheerful and was having a meal with his family. He walked

Table 4
Suicidal ideas and actions

Behaviour	Total (N = 80)
Suicide mentioned frequently and attempt made within past year	3
Suicide mentioned fairly often	4
Suicide mentioned occasionally	15
No mention of suicide	58

out of the room, and was gone for some time. When someone went to look for him he was found to have taken an overdose. This sort of unpredictability is perhaps more of a strain than anything else, and sometimes the patients seemed to feel this themselves. One young man, for example, would not allow his parents to open his bedroom window at night, because he said he was afraid he might throw himself out. His mother was particularly anxious in his case because several years before he had in fact thrown himself from a window of a high building and had almost succeeded in killing himself. At that time he said he had done it because 'a voice told me to'.

Socially embarrassing behaviour
About one third of the patients were overactive from time to time according to their relatives, rushing around the house excitedly or pouring out a stream of incoherent chatter about various unrealistic schemes or fantastic ideas. Some patients were 'jumpy' and 'fidgety', unable to settle to anything, starting on something and growing tired of it almost at once. Some would simply pace up and down the room interminably. Some would wander off and not be seen for several days or weeks, causing great anxiety to their families.

Restlessness was also a problem when it occurred at night. (See Table 5). Often relatives would be kept awake by a patient pacing about the house. One patient, a young man who lived with his parents, used to disturb their sleep by pacing up and down in his bedroom at night. However, they had found a way of preventing this. They had evolved a 'saying goodnight ritual' (as they called it). The patient's father would go and sit with the

Table 5
Restlessness at night

Behaviour	Total (N = 48)
Patient up most of every night	1
Active most nights; in bed part of the time	9
Active some nights; in bed most of the time	5
In bed all night	32
Up at night; in bed by day	1

(Information available for only 48 patients. Patients in hospital or living separately from relatives omitted.)

patient and talk to him for a while about what had happened in the day. Then his mother would look in and kiss him goodnight. The parents had found that in this way the patient felt more settled and would spend all night in bed. With some patients restlessness might take a noisier form – such as playing the same pop record over and over again very loudly. This kind of thing could not only disturb the family's sleep, but also the neighbours', which led to all sorts of secondary difficulties. Ten of the patients in the series were up and about at some time during most nights (see Table 5). There was usually little relatives could do about this kind of behaviour, as they found that if they asked the patient to stop he either took no notice or became enraged. Some resorted to indirect methods like sabotaging the record player while the patient was out of the room. Others managed to persuade the patient to be restless in a more socially acceptable way. For example, one patient used to pace up and down the road in front of the house for an hour at a time. This attracted a lot of attention from neighbours, until the relative managed to persuade her to do her pacing in the back garden where she could not be seen.

There was also a small group of patients who talked, not too little, but too much. They were described as 'compulsive talkers', who would 'chatter on for ages, and then at the end you feel baffled and think, "what on earth was all that about?" '. These individuals seemed to want to communicate, but they lacked the skills to do so. They had an odd or stilted way of expressing themselves. They might monopolise the conversation when visitors were present, chattering on and on in a rather nonsensical way, or giving 'everyone a lecture' on some rather offbeat subject currently obsessing them. Or they might attempt to join in a general conversation, but come out with odd or totally irrelevant remarks, causing a baffled and embarrassed silence. 'He's the biggest conversation stopper I know', one relative said. 'He could throw a spanner in the works of the most animated conversation', was another comment made.

These patients lack the withdrawn self-sufficiency of the more silent ones. They crave companionship and want people to listen to them, but do not have the necessary skills to achieve this. They may become very frustrated as a result, and extremely demanding of their immediate family. Usually it is the mother, being at home all day, who bears the main brunt of this. Mothers in this situation said how exhausted they become with the constant demanding of attention and the stream of confusing, often muddled, talk.

About a quarter of the patients had odd ideas of various kinds, for example, that the neighbours were plotting against them or that some particular relative was at fault. The latter could be very distressing for the relative concerned. The odd ideas often concerned agencies or organisations whom the patient believed to have power over him or to be planning to harm him. Relatives found it difficult to know what to do when a patient expressed this kind of idea. If he said he had just been pursued up the road by a secret agent, ought they to accept what he said, and pretend to believe it, or should they tell him he was imagining it? Many relatives feared that if they used the former approach they were encouraging the patient to lose touch even more with reality. But if they took the latter course, would the patient lose his confidence in them?

Sometimes a patient might ponder about visions he had seen or voices he had heard during an acute phase of the illness, even though these were no longer occurring. If he did this, a relative might fear it was a sign of the illness recurring. The relative might, therefore, tend to be rather brisk with the patient, telling him 'not to be silly' or 'you know that was only an illness'. But this approach could make the patient feel even more that nobody understood his experiences and he might therefore become frustrated and angry with the relative.

One patient, a middle-aged married lady, was relating how she had poured away several pints of milk recently, believing them to be poisoned. Her husband, who seemed very warm and tolerant towards her, but also deeply puzzled by her illness, became anxious when she spoke about this incident. He tried rather nervously to make a joke of it, saying 'wasn't that a silly thing to do Annie? Fancy wasting all that milk. I don't know'. But his wife became irritated at this, saying 'Well, what would you do if a voice told you the milk was poisoned? I mean if you heard an actual voice?' Her husband, trying to appease her now, said, 'Yes, I know it didn't seem silly at the time, but you know now it was the illness, don't you?'. His wife, however, remained doubtful, replying 'I don't know, I still don't see how a *voice* can be an illness'.

Patients tended to develop sudden irrational fears. They might, for instance, become fearful of a particular room in the house. Maybe they would tell the family the reason for their fear. 'There's a poisonous gas leaking into that room' or 'there are snakes under the bed in that room'. At first relatives are baffled by this. Some admitted they had grown frustrated with a patient's absolute refusal to abandon some idea, despite all their attempts to reason with him, and had lost their temper. But they found this only resulted in the patient becoming very upset, and in any case the idea continued to be held with as much conviction as ever.

Another focus for odd ideas was the patient's own body. Some tended to complain of curious physical symptoms. One girl was constantly stroking her neck because she said she felt as if she had a 'tight wire' running down it. Another walked with a limp, and said it was because one of her legs was shorter than the other. Relatives never knew if a patient's physical complaints were real or imagined. In this respect, a sympathetic and understanding general practitioner was an invaluable asset.

Several subjects talked or laughed to themselves, but did this only in their own rooms, and not in front of their family. 'If you stand outside his room you can hear that he's keeping up a more or less constant monologue in there'. 'Sometimes I hear shrieks of laughter coming from her room'. Others, however, would sit throughout a meal laughing to themselves, regardless of who was there. Some would occasionally cry out in great distress in reaction to hallucinatory voices. A few relatives had been able to persuade a patient that he must not behave in this way in public. If he forgot and started to do it when others were present, a discreet reminder from the relative would silence him, or else he would go off somewhere alone until he had finished his muttering.

Other examples of embarrassing behaviour given were constant cadging of cigarettes from visitors, making personal remarks or walking out of the room in the middle of a conversation. In some cases, the behaviour was even more public; shouting in the street in response to hallucinatory voices, or a patient might start swearing at someone whom he thought to be persecuting him. If he had delusional ideas about the neighbours, he might call on them and create a scene. Relatives described how some patients would sit in peculiar, awkward-looking postures. Others would sit with a leg swinging constantly up and down. Several relatives said that the patient walked in an odd way – 'very stiffly', or 'lopsided', or perhaps with hands held out at odd angles. Other habits included grimacing, working the mouth round continually, and rocking backwards and forwards in a chair. Often these habits were irritating and some relatives tried to stop them. A few found that an affectionately teasing approach was sometimes effective, but on the whole relatives seemed resigned to this sort of behaviour and accepted it.

Threats and violence, including verbal abuse, violence to property and to persons were fortunately uncommon and most incidents that did occur were minor. Most patients were the reverse of violent. They were in fact extremely timid and disliked any show of anger. Relatives often said that a patient would refuse to watch anything even slightly violent on T.V. Some relatives had to be very careful never to show a trace of irritability towards the patient because he would become distressed by this.

In other instances, however, the problem of violence could make life impossible in the household. Some patients confined themselves to verbal abuse and threats. The constant antagonism was very wearing, especially for a lone relative. One said, 'The only time he talks to me is when he wants to bully me'. Often patients blamed their family for their illness. Some patients were violent to property, breaking windows for example. Sometimes relatives could trace back the reason for the violence to some recent frustration the patient had suffered; for example, to an unsuccessful attempt to join in some social activity. At other times the violence occurred quite unpredictably. Nine patients had been physically violent to relatives within the previous year. If there had ever been an incident of this kind, even though it had been years before, the possibility that further violence might occur always seemed to persist, though it might be very much in the background. Some relatives had found they were able to take a very firm line over violence. They made it clear that violence was beyond the limit and that if it occurred the patient would have to go into hospital. The cooperation of doctors was useful in this respect.

Only a very small number of patients presented sexual problems; most in fact showing a total disinterest in sex. A very small number had created problems by making sexual advances to relatives. The numbers are too small for any generalisation, but it seemed that when relatives had spoken to doctors or social workers about this they had not received a sympathetic hearing and possibly had not been believed. On the whole, however, relatives were delighted at any sign of normal sexuality.

Overall scores on bahavioural abnormality
These detailed illustrations of the kinds of abnormal behaviour described by relatives do not give an overall picture of the frequency and severity of disturbance. Two crude indices were therefore used; one taking into account all the behaviour described under the heading of social withdrawal, the other summarising the behaviour described under the heading of socially embarrassing behaviour. For each case, ratings on the constituent items were summed and expressed as percentages of the total possible score. Cut-off points were arbitrarily selected to represent different degrees of severity. The results are given in Table 6. Behaviour associated with social withdrawal is clearly very common; 90 % of the patients are described as showing at least a moderate degree of it, nearly one in three in severe form. Socially embarrassing behaviour is not present at all, or only in minimal degree, in nearly a third of cases. About half the patients show this behaviour to a moderate extent and about one fifth show it to a severe degree.

Table 6
Severity of Socially Withdrawn and Socially Embarrassing Behaviour

Characteristic	Total (N = 80)	
Social Withdrawal, etc.		%
None or slight (0–10%)	8	10
Moderate (11–40%)	49	61
Marked (41%+)	23	29
Socially Embarrassing Behaviour		
None or slight (0–10%)	27	34
Moderate (11–40%)	38	48
Marked (41%+)	14	18
Not known	1	1

The impact on relatives will be described in subsequent sections.

Social Performance

The previous section illustrated the impairments of schizophrenic patients in behaviour, thought and mood. In this section, we shall be concerned with the degree of impairment in the performance of social roles and duties. The assessment of severity was made by the interviewer after obtaining a systematic description of the patient's performance of social, occupational and domestic roles, in order to try to make the ratings comparable with each other, in spite of the varying level of expectation on the part of relatives. The 15 patients who had been in hospital for three months or more at the time of interview were not included in this assessment. Married patients living with their husbands or wives are dealt with in a separate section.

Single Patients

Three main areas of social performance were considered: contribution to running the domestic economy of the household, ability to provide emotional support and companionship to others in the household, and competence in social relationships outside the household. Table 7 summarises the results.

Table 7
Competence in performance of social roles:

Patients not living with spouse

Social Role	Fully satis-factory	Fairly satis-factory	Rather unsatis-factory	Very unsatis-factory	Total No.	% unsatis-factory
Household economy shared with						
relative	1	6	16	13	36⎫	
living alone	1	—	3	2	12⎭	71
Companionship and support	3	13	15	15	46*	65
Social mixing outside household	2	12	28	6	48	71

*Two of the patients living on their own were not in regular contact with relatives and have therefore been omitted from this assessment.

Household economy

The 12 patients who were living on their own are shown separately under the heading of 'household economy', because they had to look after themselves. Most of these were managing fairly satisfactorily. Nevertheless, most of them did in fact cope only with the help of relatives. One relative said that she had come to dread the ring of the telephone in case it heralded yet another crisis. The fact that her son was not living at home did not reduce her anxiety; in some respects, it was increased. Many of these patients were both dependent and unpredictable in behaviour and the relatives were as tense as if the patient had still been living at home. The points made in the following paragraphs are therefore applicable in general.

Contributions to the household economy were assessed in terms of financial and service help. One third of the patients at home made no contributions of these kinds: no money, no help with cooking, cleaning, shopping or other chores. Some patients did have an income, e.g. from sickness and supplementary benefit, but did not give any of this to the relatives. Others refused to collect the benefit. One mother said, 'I often think I should ask him for money, but the trouble is, the less money he has, the less likely he is to go out of the house. So I tend to give him money just to get him out for a while'. In another case, the patient's father complained that the patient did nothing to help his mother in the house but, on the very rare occasions when he did make some small contribution, 'he'll present it to one in the evening as if it were some great triumph: "I did the washing up after tea, today", he'll say, as if he had done something wonderful'. This comment also illustrates the problems that parents had in knowing how to respond to such situations.

Another large group of patients made some contribution to the household economy but this was inadequate in relation to what they took out of it. For example, the mother of one young man took charge of his weekly income from sickness benefit, returning him some pocket money. He would wash up or mow the lawn if asked to do so but tended to stop half-way through the job and wander away. Supervising him took more effort than the job itself. He never offered to do anything.

In only 6 cases out of 36 could the patient's contribution be called fairly satisfactory. One patient, for example, regularly gave part of his weekly benefit to his mother to help pay for his keep. He always made his own bed and sometimes helped with the vacuum-cleaning and the shopping. Only one patient was regarded as making a fully adequate contribution to the domestic economy. He attended a day centre but cleaned the flat each morning before leaving, made his own bed and cooked breakfast for himself and his sister. He did the shopping on the way to the centre and gave his sister all his weekly money. As she was an old age pensioner this contribution was relatively substantial.

Companionship and support
It can be seen from Table 7 that patients were almost as impaired in their ability to provide companionship and emotional support to relatives as in their competence in the domestic field. Clearly the degree of handicap of a given individual will not necessarily be equal in all fields of social performance. Someone who is unable to contribute much financially or in the way of effective household work may nevertheless be a loyal and emotionally warm companion. In fact, his or her other handicaps are more likely to be acceptable in such a case and the relatives are less likely to feel themselves useless and unable to help. On the other

hand, if a patient gave no hint of response to the relative's friendly overtures, or was hostile or irritable, the relative would feel emotionally drained and would eventually cease to expect any companionship or support at all. It was thought that, in most cases, the relative did actually try to offer friendly contact but no attempt was made to judge the quality of this since we were mainly interested in the patients' contribution to the relationship.

In two thirds of cases the patients seemed almost or completely cut off. As one mother said, 'You just can't understand it. Here's someone you've known all these years and you've always got on well with, and suddenly he can't even stand being in the same room with you'. Many relatives came to accept this 'one-way relationship' but they remained puzzled, dissatisfied and often guilty. One patient returned home each evening from the day centre, ate, in complete silence, the meal her aunt provided and then went straight up to her room. 'She doesn't speak to me or tell me anything she's done during the day' said her aunt, who was lonely and elderly and would have been very glad of a chat in the evenings. She was puzzled by the patient's almost total lack of communication. 'If she'd only unburden herself and tell me what's on her mind, I'm sure she'd be better. I can't make out if she's unhappy or what. I ask her sometimes: "Are you happy?" But she just nods'.

Not only did this patient fail to offer any companionship to her aunt, but she also seemed to have little use for the friendship her aunt wished to offer. This makes things doubly difficult for the relatives. Many found that, even if there was no other emotional satisfaction for them in the relationship, it helped their morale greatly to feel they were needed. So if the relative felt the patient had some positive feelings towards him and valued his friendship, this could help the relative to endure a certain amount of difficult and demanding behaviour. But if the patient seemed indifferent towards the relative, or indeed positively rejected his friendship, then the relative could find his relationship with the patient draining and exhausting.

In the remaining third of cases the patient could offer such emotional 'rewards' to the relative, but usually only rarely. 'Just for a little while he'll be back to his old self again, and you realise that somewhere he's still there, in spite of all his illness and everything'. Others were emotionally very dependent on the relative all the time, though they were able to offer the relative little in the way of adult companionship. A few patients were able to sustain a normal emotional relationship with the relative. 'She's a very pleasant person to live with now, very sweet and considerate', one relative said of a patient whose illness had abated after a prolonged difficult period.

Social mixing outside the home

Nearly three-quarters of the patients had great difficulty in mixing socially when away from home with people other than close relatives. Only 6 actually shunned the company of others altogether. One, for example, said, 'I don't like mixing with people. I've got nothing to say to them'. These six were very much enclosed within their own world, and seemed to have no desire at all for companionship apart from what was available at home. A much larger number did show some need for social contact but it was usually exiguous and they lacked the social skills necessary to produce a rewarding response from other people. For example, one patient liked his brother and sister-in-law and their children to pay a visit. After a brief period of playing with the children, however, this patient would then go away and lie down, not reappearing before the visitors had left. Another patient was afraid to go to any social gathering alone but was eager to accompany her mother. (Her mother found this a bit wearing, since there was seldom any opportunity to go visiting by herself). Once the patient reached the destination, however, she took no part in any social interaction and never volunteered a word of her own.

About a quarter of the patients did show some social initiative and skill and were able to sustain some kind of social contact outside the family circle, though this was maintained rather precariously and relationships thus formed tended to be detached and transitory. Only two patients achieved a number of fairly lasting and satisfying social contacts with anyone other than relatives.

In most cases where there some social contacts outside the home, this was due to the fact that the relatives belonged to bridge or tennis clubs, or other social groups, in which the patient could also play some part.

Table 8
Competence in performance of social roles:

Married patients living with spouse

Social Role	Fully satisfactory	Fairly satisfactory	Rather unsatisfactory	Very unsatisfactory	Total No.	% unsatisfactory
Household economy	3	9	4	—	16	25
Companionship and support	1	5	5	2	13	54
Social mixing outside household	4	3	5	3	15	53
Partner's sexual satisfaction	—	6	—	4	10	40
Parental roles	—	7	4	—	11	36

*There were 16 married patients living with a spouse. In some cases the social performance is not known; in others the item is not applicable, e.g. the patient had no children.

Married Patients

In general, married patients living with a spouse were rated more highly on social performance than single patients, as Table 8 shows. The very fact of marriage, of course, argues a degree of social competence that many single patients lack. Seven men and nine women were married. The results will be discussed in less detail than for the single patients because of the small numbers.

No married patients were described as contributing *nothing* to the domestic economy of the household and only four out of 16 were described as contributing little. Even unemployed husbands did contribute through sickness or unemployment benefit and helped about the house. Housewives did usually perform some of their social role. On the other hand, only three patients were regarded as quite unimpaired. Most were mildly handicapped as, for example, one housewife who had spells every few weeks in which she could do very little but who usually recovered within a day or so. Another patient was described by her husband as being very forgetful. She could start to fill the oil-stove and then go on to something else and forget, so that the stove overflowed. One husband had been an in-patient for more than 10 years and was now unemployed, living at home. His wife accepted that she was the breadwinner and, though their combined income was low, the reversal of the role caused no discontent. Where the couple were younger, or where there were small children, however, unemployment in the man or lapses in domestic performance by the woman were more likely to cause tension.

The rating of the patients' ability to provide emotional support and companionship showed more impairment; just over half were unsatisfactory in this respect although only 2 out of 13 were regarded as providing no support whatever. The spouse complained of being 'emotionally drained' or that the relationship was 'stagnant', that they were 'worn down' with the constant effort of supporting the patient but receiving little support in return. Many husbands or wives wanted to feel that the patient needed them and it appears that a patient's ability to 'reward' a spouse in this way is an important factor in maintaining a marriage. One husband said that one of the worst things was 'to feel you can't get through to her however hard you try'. A wife, who had been 'rewarded' by her husband, said: 'I think they need you more with this illness than when they've got a physical illness'. Another wife said: 'If a man's ill, then you make allowances. I know he doesn't want to know me when he's ill, but he wants me to be there all the same. Then as soon as he's better he's the kindest man you could know'.

So far as social mixing outside the household was concerned, the informants varied a good deal as to how much they expected their partners to undertake. Some were content to stay at home and make very little outside social contact. In such cases, the patient's impairments were not very evident. Others complained bitterly of the curtailment of their social lives. One wife said, 'We never get invited anywhere more than once'. Another wife tried to get the patient to accompany her to a club occasionally in the evenings but they always had to leave after half an hour or so because the patient thought people were staring at him and talking about him. In about half the cases, the marital partners described a fairly satisfactory situation in respect of social mixing, but in the other half things were rather unsatisfactory.

The sexual satisfaction experienced by the spouse of a schizophrenic patient is rarely discussed partly, perhaps, because the marital partners themselves do not wish to speak of it. In several cases, it was not possible to make any assessment because the answers were vague or off-putting. Out of 10 cases where a rating was made, 6 patients seemed to give a fair degree of satisfaction but this assumption is based on answers much as 'Things are all right'. Four people spoke of a serious impairment due to the patient having lost all sexual interest. One husband expressed this very bitterly: 'She would sleep with any man she'd meet in the street before she would sleep with me'. He did not, however, have any specific evidence of his wife's infidelity.

Only 11 married patients had children in the household. In four cases they performed their parental role rather unsatisfactorily. Thus one husband described how he found his small son playing with the lighted oil-stove while his wife was simply sitting staring into space. Patients were sometimes irritable and impatient with their children. One would send her son to his uncle with messages such as, 'Come quickly! My mother says she is dying'. The grown-up daughter of a patient recalled how frightened she had been when, as a child, her mother had said she was going to drown herself. A husband complained that his wife sat talking to hallucinatory voices in front of their six-year-old son, who would say to her: 'Who are you talking to? Your mind isn't right'. Discipline was another problem mentioned. One relative complained that a patient's teenage son was allowed to do as he pleased. He would laugh at his mother and say: 'My mum is crackers'. It seems that in this instance the patient's husband was doing little to help with the problem. In another instance, where a patient's husband had carefully explained to his teenage son about the illness, the son was most solicitous towards his mother. But this too might lead to its own problems, if the son were to become overburdened with anxiety about her. In general, although the performance of a parental role was regarded as 'fairly satisfactory' in seven out of eleven cases, most patients did experience difficulties and the spouse quite often had to take on a large proportion of the parental tasks. It was when this compensation did not occur that problems arose with the children.

Overall Scores on Social Performance

Table 9 shows how patients were distributed in terms of overall scores on social performance. Married patients living with a spouse were clearly much more competent than the rest; in 11

Table 9
Overall Scores on Social Performance

Performance *Single patients*	Total (N = 48)
Very good (81–100%)	–
Quite good (61–80%)	4
Fair (41–60%)	17
Rather poor (21–40%)	18
Very poor (0–20%)	9
Married patients	(N = 16)
Very good	2
Quite good	3
Fair	6
Rather poor	5
Very poor	–

cases out of 16, performance was fair or good, though the category 'fair' conceals some potentially stressful impairments. None was regarded as performing very poorly. However, of the 48 patients who were living alone or with other kin, 27 (56%) were rated as showing a poor or very poor social performance.

Personal Problems Described by Relatives

Relatives' attitudes towards patients

In this section we shall be concerned with the personal problems described by relatives which were due to the fact that someone with schizophrenia was living within the household or was very closely associated with it. That relatives were very definitely affected by these problems may be seen from Table 10 which summarises the effects that relatives thought they had had on their own health or well-being. No fewer than 30% of relatives thought that the effects had been 'very severe' and another 18% thought they had been 'severe'.

Despite these effects the majority of relatives showed a tolerant or positively accepting attitude towards the patient. A judgement was made about the relative's general attitude towards the patient as revealed by the way he or she spoke about the patient during the interview (see Table 11). No relatives were

Table 10

Degree of impairment of relatives' own health or well-being, attributed to problems connected with schizophrenia

Severity of impairment	Total (N = 80)
None	15
Moderate	27
Severe	14
Very Severe	24

Table 11

Relatives' attitude towards the patient

	Total
Rejecting	—
Unfavourable	20
Indifferent	3
Tolerant	34
Accepting	23

considered to be 'rejecting'. This is not surprising, as only patients who were still in contact with a relative were included in this study. About a quarter of the relatives were 'unfavourable' in their attitude to the patient in the sense that they spoke in a critical or censorious way (though this might well be with good reason).

An example of a relative who was 'unfavourable' in her attitude towards the patient was Elizabeth N. She was nineteen years old and shared a council flat with her mother, the patient, who was forty-six. Elizabeth could not remember how her mother's illness had begun, but thought she must have been about six years old at the time. She had spent a large part of her childhood living with her grandmother as her mother had been in hospital.

Elizabeth seemed to be a competent and self-possessed young woman, in many ways unusually mature for her age. She took her responsibility for her mother very seriously. During the day Elizabeth worked at a clerical job, while her mother attended a local day centre. Elizabeth's mother was slow in movement and overweight. She wore a shapeless and rather dirty dress, her hair did not look as if it had been combed, and she had a vacant expression.

Elizabeth described how her mother would sit with her in the evening while she watched television. Her mother never seemed to watch it but simply stared into space. From time to time she would mutter to herself, or suddenly start to laugh. Elizabeth said this got on her nerves. 'Can you imagine watching T.V. with someone who suddenly starts to laugh at nothing?' she said, 'it drives you round the twist'. Another problem which annoyed Elizabeth a great deal was her mother's incontinence. This had been particularly bad recently, and her mother had been 'smelling awful and her clothes were ruined'. The whole house had also begun to smell so that Elizabeth did not like to invite any friends round. Elizabeth refused to have anything to do with her mother's bed-linen. 'I leave that entirely to her', she said, 'though I'm sure her mattress must be rotten by now'. Elizabeth also complained about her mother's untidiness. 'She'll knock over a cup of coffee or spill the sugar all over the floor and then she'll just leave it there for me to clear up'.

Despite this unfavourable attitude towards her mother, Elizabeth felt a strong sense of duty towards her. She continued to live with her despite all the tensions and restrictions it imposed upon her. She rarely went away at weekends although she would have liked to do so, because 'I know she'll be there all alone'. Her main wish was that some kind of hostel placement could be found for her mother. She thought this would suit her mother as 'she seems contented when she's in hospital. She seems to like the routine and having things done for her'. Looking ahead, Elizabeth felt some solution of this kind would have to be found, because she could not envisage continuing to live with her mother in the future, if she were to get married.

It can be seen from this example, that because a relative's attitude was 'unfavourable' this did not necessarily mean that he or she did not accept responsibility for the patient. It did mean however that the relative would have been very glad if the services could have removed some of the weight of such a responsibility. In other instances, however, relatives were tolerant or positively accepting of a patient, and glad to have him living in the household. One example of such relatives were Mr. and Mrs. R. (both in their seventies) whose son Robert, aged forty, lived with them in a council prefab. He had been ill since the age of about nineteen. His handicaps mainly took the form of withdrawal, although prior to his last hospitalisation (a year previously) he had been talking to voices, and behaving oddly.

Robert's mother said he had had more jobs than she could remember and had never kept any for long. His current job had lasted a fortnight but he was already complaining about it and saying he was not happy. As Robert's parents were both old age pensioners it must have made quite a difference to their finances if Robert was not in work. However, this did not seem to worry them, and his mother said, 'I take things in my stride. I was brought up the hard way so I don't worry about these things'. Robert's mother said she would have liked to be able to get out more but she would not leave Robert alone because 'you never know. He might suddenly go'. She was anxious because the last time he relapsed Robert went wandering off walking down the middle of a busy road.

Robert was sometimes depressed and said he should never have been born. His mother was puzzled by this but tried to talk him out of it if she could. Robert was also underactive. When he was not at work he would spend most of the day dozing in the chair. Again, his mother accepted this and did not disapprove of such behaviour. She also said Robert was very overweight, but she did not worry about this. 'What I think is, if you're fat, you're fat,' she said. In general Robert's parents accepted his handicaps without resentment. 'We're not the kind of parents to holler and shout and nag at him' his mother said. They said they liked his company and would not have been without him.

It can be seen from these examples that some relatives can face considerable difficulties simply coping with everyday behaviour. Certainly, many relatives felt that living day in and day out with the often strange and irrational behaviour of somebody suffering from schizophrenia had taken its toll of them emotionally. Many said that they had, at one time or another, felt near to a breakdown themselves.

In speaking about their personal difficulties, relatives mentioned problems in three main areas: firstly, their own emotional reactions; secondly, conflicts arising within family relationships; thirdly, problems encountered by the family within the wider community. Problems in each one of these three areas tended to rebound upon each other. For example, a family could become isolated through the difficulties involved in trying to maintain a normal social life. There would then be no external safety valve to the family to relieve tension; the family would lack friends who could help out and add their resources to those of the family in times of stress. Thus interfamilial conflict, and each family member's own emotional difficulties, could be exacerbated. Conversely, a diminution in any one of these three areas of difficulty could relieve pressure upon the other two.

Emotional reactions of relatives

Most relatives referred to some form of emotional stress, though they differed in how articulate they were about this. But among the different descriptions they gave of the emotional stresses the illness had brought for them, anxiety, guilt, depression, and anger were frequently mentioned.

Many relatives felt that anxiety constituted the main strain which they experienced. Often it arose because it was so hard to judge how the patient was feeling at any given time, or how he was likely to react to any given situation. Because nobody ever knew quite what to expect from the patient, the atmosphere in the household might become generally tense and jumpy.

The patient's 'unpredictability' was mentioned so often as a severe strain that it deserves further consideration. Probably everyone requires a certain amount of order in life. Most of us tend to take this for granted and are scarcely aware of it. But if a patient is highly unpredictable, then this seems to have a rebounding effect upon others closely involved with him. To be constantly 'living on the edge of a volcano' (an analogy several relatives used) must take its toll of even the most placid of personalities. This seemed to apply as much when the patient was living separately from the relative as it did when he was actually resident in the household. If the patient was living elsewhere, than the constant fear of some kind of crisis occurring out of the blue could be just as anxiety-provoking.

On an everyday level, a patient's unpredictable habits could disrupt the routine of a household. One father explained how difficult it was for his wife to run the household. 'You need some kind of routine,' he said, 'I don't mean a strict routine or anything, but my wife will cook a meal, and then he doesn't want it. Then two hours later he suddenly decides he does.' In this case, the patient's mother had his younger brothers and sisters to see to as well as the patient, and she was not at all in good health herself. This kind of constant disorganisation of even a minimal routine made life very difficult.

A further cause of anxiety was the patients' unpredictability of mood. With some patients, relatives found: 'You just never know what he's going to be like from one hour to the next'. One mother spoke of how she woke up every morning dreading the day ahead, in case her son had one of his 'bad days'. Relatives spoke of being 'constantly on a knife-edge', 'always having to watch what you say', and 'living on your nerves'. This constant fear of the unexpected was particularly severe if relatives remembered some incident in the past when the patient had done something terrible completely out of the blue, and for no apparent reason. One father, for example, recounted how he had once been taking his son somewhere in the car. There had been no sign that anything was amiss, nor had anything happened to upset the patient that day. But when the father turned around to reverse, the patient suddenly punched him hard, breaking his nose. This kind of incident need only have happened once for relatives to have it permanently at the back of their minds, making them always slightly uneasy and watchful of the patient's reactions. The unpredictable always tends to be frightening and because the patients often seemed to respond to internal rather than external stimuli, this could give the relatives a panicky feeling of having no control at all over the situation.

As well as the constant fear of a sudden outburst, and perhaps violence, from the patient, relatives also worried about what the patient might do to himself. A few patients, for example, had a habit of wandering off, walking down the middle of the road, when they felt ill. They could easily be knocked down by traffic. Worries about the patient's ability to look after himself could be even more of a problem if the patient lived on his own, away from the relative.

There were also the more long-term worries about the patient's future which relatives frequently expressed. The older the parents the more this (very realistic) anxiety preoccupied them. Not many shared the sanguine faith of the Camberwell mother, who said, 'I suppose I worry sometimes about what will happen to him when I'm gone, but really I know he'll be all right, because the Welfare will look after him'. Some were so anxious about the patient's dependence upon them, and his inability to cope with life on his own, that they tended to communicate this anxiety to the patient, who could become equally worried. Parents often said how much they wished there were some kind of sheltered hostel, where the patient would be well-cared for when they were too old to cope with him. As it was, they had many fears about him sliding downhill once he no longer had them, perhaps becoming a vagrant if he did not spend the rest of his days in hospital.

The relatives therefore tended to live in a permanently anxiety-provoking situation. The older relatives had in fact got more to worry about, and also said they found their ability to tolerate anxiety and strain was diminishing rapidly with their advancing years. Elderly or young, however, the continual worry took its toll of relatives emotionally.

As well as anxiety, many relatives mentioned guilt and depression when describing their emotional reactions to the patient's illness. It seems probable that in our society, guilt is the common reaction of a parent to any abnormality or sign of illness in a child, and this is functional insofar as it makes the parent endeavour to do something about the situation. But with schizophrenia various additional factors tend to exacerbate guilty feelings to the point where they become disabling. Often, for example, the patient would go through a phase of blaming his parents for his illness, and verbally abusing them about it. Or sometimes doctors or social workers implied that the patient's parents were to blame for his breakdown. Nor were feelings of guilt restricted only to the past. Several relatives mentioned that one of the greatest strains was never knowing if they were doing the right thing. Some worried constantly about this, so that their daily routine was permeated with guilty feelings about whether they were dealing with difficult behaviour in the correct way. Guilt could grow to such an extent that the relative became very depressed, and it could destroy the relative's ability to cope.

The guilt relatives felt was linked closely to the fact that certain achievements in life (such as marriage, and a job) are generally regarded socially as highly important. Parents tended particularly to feel they were to blame for the patient's social failure, and felt this failure as their own. They saw themselves as worthless and inadequate. Some expressed these feelings by saying that they wished they and the patient might all be killed. Depression, like guilt, could become a permanent state of mind. 'You never really enjoy yourself,' one mother said, 'because it's always at the back of your mind the whole of the time. You're never free of it'. Another said, 'You've got all the ties and constant demands on your time, that you get with a small child. You accept it with a child because it's all for a purpose and you know one day that child will be independent of you, because of what you've done. But with this there's never going to be an end result. You know it'll just go on and on and he'll never be any different'. It was this feeling of pointlessness and of so much effort expended uselessly that left relatives emotionally exhausted and depressed.

Often, the relatives' depression also had to do with feelings of loss and grief. If, for example, a son or daughter had shown a great deal of promise in earlier years, then parents felt much grief to see him so handicapped now, and no longer able to make use of his talents. These feelings were probably not helped if the patient occasionally reverted to being 'his old self again', as some relatives described. One mother, for example, spoke of how there was usually a constant tension in the air when the patient was there. 'You're so careful not to say the wrong thing, and yet sooner or later he always takes something amiss'. But then she went on to recount how, 'Sometimes, out of the blue, he'll suddenly say something very nice like "Thank you for that meal mother, it was lovely. Nobody can cook like you!"' But this kind of unexpected let-up in the usually antagonistic attitude of a difficult patient did not always help the situation in the long run. It could remind the relatives of what the patient had been like before the illness, and cause them to re-experience their grief and sense of loss. It could also raise the relatives' hopes, making them think the patient might soon once again be as he was before the illness.

In fact, several relatives mentioned that giving up hope had paradoxically been the turning point for them in coming to terms with their unhappiness. 'Once you give up hope,' one mother said, 'you start to perk up. Once you realise he'll never be cured you start to relax'. These relatives had lowered their expectations and aspirations for the patient, and had found that doing this had been the first step in cutting the problem down to a manageable size.

Irritation and anger were another emotional reaction which several relatives had experienced. Some patients, for example, showed a total lack of initiative, which was extremely annoying, and 'would try the patience of a saint' (as one father put it). One relative described how she had to tell the patient 'every little thing ... even if his dinner is ready and on the table, you have to say, "Get the chair and put it to the table. Sit down on it, and eat your dinner" – if you don't tell him all that he'll just stand there staring at you vacantly'. Annoying mannerisms, compulsive chattering, or aimless wandering about the house, were other examples of the kinds of behaviour which could be highly irritating to live with.

As well as suffering a constant build up of small irritations, relatives could also be deeply angry and resentful at the way things had turned out. The disappointment of seeing the patient so disabled (especially if he had once seemed to have a great deal of potential) could embitter relatives. 'It's such a waste of a life,' was a frequent comment. Perhaps this kind of feeling lay behind remarks like 'He's nothing but a layabout,' or 'It's not illness, it's bone idleness'.

The constant anxiety, the guilt, depression, disappointment, and frustration or anger at the insoluble nature of the problem were all emotions frequently described. It is not necessary to regard these emotional reactions as 'abnormal' or in some sense pathological in themselves. They can be seen simply as reactions to a confusing, incomprehensible, distressing and apparently unmodifiable situation. Nevertheless, they are reactions potentially destructive of coping ability, and can become self-generating. This was not always the case. Some relatives felt they had come to terms with their feelings about the illness, and the effect it had had on their lives. However, this generally seemed to go along with the relatives having worked out ways to manage the patient and his behaviour having become reasonably predictable. It tended to be the result of years of trial-and-error, and a great deal of patience.

The way the relatives were feeling was a very important factor in the kind of environment in which the patient lived. If, for example, the relative was so depressed he had given up trying, then the patient might well deteriorate, through having no consistent standard of behaviour expected of him. In this way, the patient's deterioration and the relative's depression would become linked in a downward spiral. Intervention from an outside agency is required in such a case, but if the relative is emotionally exhausted, then the chances are that he will not have the motivation or the energy to seek help from the services which could break into the vicious circle.

Conflicts in family relationships

Illness within a family always causes some difficulties. It means one member of the family is 'out of action' in certain ways, so that others have to take over his tasks for him for a while. He needs extra attention and others must have less than usual. While he is ill, routine generally is upset. With schizophrenia, these effects can be very marked, and go on for a long time.

Several relatives mentioned the divisive effects of schizophrenia upon a family. For example, parents with a son or daughter who was a patient might find their loyalties divided between the patient and his brothers and sisters. One mother said she had not fully realised the distress a patient was causing to his younger brother, until this brother one day told her how much he dreaded the school holidays, and looked forward to term beginning again so that he could get away from the patient. In another case, there was constant friction between a patient and her younger sister. They were always quarrelling, and the parents feared the patient might one day injure her sister, as she could be physically aggressive at times.

Another problem was that patients often felt bitter when they saw their younger siblings achieving things they had not been able to do. One patient became very resentful of his younger brother when the latter began to have girlfriends. In another case, the younger sister of a patient wanted to learn to drive but the parents did not know whether to allow this, as they knew the patient would be jealous and demand to be allowed to learn too. But the parents felt sure this patient could never be trusted with a car.

In some instances where the relative interviewed was a parent, it emerged during the interview that another child of the family was also mentally ill, or demonstrating signs of severe disturbance. In the Camberwell group, two of the patients had a sibling also diagnosed as schizophrenic. In the Fellowship group, five of the patients had a sibling showing marked signs of disturbance (that is, a sibling who was having some form of psychiatric treatment, or who had been exhibiting very odd behaviour for a long period). This should not necessarily be attributable directly to the patient. In some cases, the siblings' difficulties had ante-dated the patient's. However, it does imply that where one member of a family suffers from schizophrenia there is quite a high risk of other members suffering some form of disturbance, whatever may be the direction of cause and effect.

As well as the problems the illness could create between siblings, it could also place strains upon the relationship between parents. In trying to cope with these emotional strains, each in his own way could end up at loggerheads with the other. For example, the father, frustrated at the insoluble nature of the problem, might fall into a state of 'permanent anger' with the patient, and with the mother's 'soft attitude' towards him. The mother, for her part, might become permanently depressed, blaming herself, and being blamed for everything. It is sometimes thought that problems and difficulties can, in the long run, strengthen a marriage and the unity between two partners, rather than weakening it. Parents were not specifically asked about this, but there were very few who gave the impression that they felt the illness had overall contributed something positive to their marriage.

It was not only within the nuclear family that conflicts arose. The extended family could also be affected. Sometimes, the patient had alienated an uncle or aunt, or sometimes a large number of relatives outside the nuclear family. Other relatives might be very tolerant, for instance, of the fact that the patient did not work. When this did happen, it could be quite serious, as families needed all the extra help they could get. When other relatives *were* helpful this could mean a great deal to the patient's close relatives, as it sometimes meant they could take an occasional break or have a holiday. The individual suffering from schizophrenia tends to fail, even at best, to achieve the minimum standards of socially expected behaviour and, at worst, will act in a positively anti-social way. This is how relatives outside the nuclear family can be alienated, and the close relatives are therefore cut off from an important potential supply of help.

Special problems arose when some of the other members of the family were children. Schizophrenia could have a disruptive effect on relationships within the family, and a permanent state of conflict and unhappiness could result, if not, indeed, total breakup of the family unit. While some families did seem able to cope with all this, they tended to be those where the patient had had a long history of illness and had also become relatively stable and manageable, and where the relatives, through various fortunate circumstances, had been able to devise a regime within which the patient could function satisfactorily.

Problems for relatives within the wider community

Some relatives said that their work had been affected. Some had had to take a less demanding job than they would have chosen if they had not had an extra drain on their time and energy. A few had had to retire early because extra help was needed at home, or because the strains of a job at the same time as having to care for the patient were simply too much. Some mentioned the importance of an understanding employer who would be sympathetic if days off were needed at short notice. However, the majority reported no effects on work, many saying that they had always been determined that their jobs would not be affected.

More relatives complained of restrictions on social life and more might have done so except that they did not expect much of a social life in any case. Some relatives felt that they had become cut off from a normal social life because of the patient's anti-social behaviour. For example, they might feel doubtful about inviting visitors to their homes because they were afraid the patient might do something to embarrass them. Those patients who were not liable to behave in a positively embarrassing way might cause just as much social awkwardness by ignoring guests completely or by sitting in complete silence all evening. Often relatives felt they had to know people very well before they could invite them to their homes. New social contacts were often just as much of a problem since sooner or later the conversation was bound to turn to, 'And do you have any children? ... Oh yes, and what does your son do?' 'Mention mental illness,' one relative said, 'and an awful hush descends on the whole room'.

Some of the patients were very attention-seeking and resented their mothers having interests outside the home. One mother said she had to leave a telephone number where she could be contacted whenever she went to visit a friend, and as often as not she would have to cut the visit short, because her schizophrenic daughter would phone after a short while and ask her on some pretext to come home again. Some mothers firmly ear-marked certain evenings in the week when they went off to some social activity, such as a club, or evening class. But often they could not accept a spontaneous invitation to go somewhere else afterwards, because the patient would be expecting them home at a certain time and would become distressed if this was not adhered to. Mothers also mentioned the awkwardness of explaining their refusal of such an invitation. People thought it very odd that somebody had to be home dead on time because her thirty-year-old son was expecting her.

In fact, a common difficulty for relatives, both at work and in leisure time, lay in the attitudes towards mental illness which are currently widely prevalent in our society. Some relatives feared they would lose their jobs if it were known that they were related to someone suffering from schizophrenia. Relatives found mental illness was frequently regarded as something totally disastrous and unmentionable. As one husband put it, 'When our friends heard about my wife's breakdown, they seemed to look on it as some kind of catastrophe – they seemed to take the attitude that she'd never be right again – never be able to go out again or anything'.

Such attitudes usually arise through ignorance, and perhaps through association of the word 'schizophrenia' with sensational articles and stories in newspapers and other media. One relative mentioned that she usually said, 'My son suffers from depression,' if people asked, because this seemed to be a more socially acceptable condition than schizophrenia. The stigma which becomes associated with mental illness can result in the family becoming cut off from the wider community and forced to rely upon its own resources.

Table 12
Relatives' satisfaction with services

Degree of satisfaction	Total (N = 80)	%
Satisfied	20	25
Moderately dissatisfied	35	44
Very dissatisfied	25	31

What Services would be Helpful?

A substantial section of the interview was concerned with the relatives' experience of services. Table 12 shows the degree of overall satisfaction with which relatives viewed the services they had experienced. Only one-fifth expressed themselves as satisfied and most of these, naturally enough, were part of the Camberwell group. Nearly one-third were very dissatisfied; mostly members of the National Schizophrenia Fellowship. Several themes came up time and again, and each will be considered in turn.

The initial contact with services

Many relatives complained about difficulties in obtaining help at the very beginning, when preventive measures might have perhaps been effective. To illustrate the kind of experiences that were common, it may be useful to consider a 'typical' history of a young patient's illness.

The young man begins to act oddly. At first his parents are not sure if they really have grounds for anxiety or whether, perhaps, they are getting things out of proportion. Then things get worse; perhaps he loses his job, disappears for days at a time, talks in a bizarre way, relates fantastic-sounding events which he claims have happened to him. Perhaps he shuts himself in his room for days on end, refusing meals and neglecting himself. His parents by now are very anxious; probably they have never heard of anyone behaving in this way before.

At this point it is quite likely that the parents will contact their G.P. The G.P. then assesses the patient's condition and if he is very ill he is admitted to hospital. If not, the patient is referred to a psychiatrist on an outpatient basis, and a social worker from the hospital or from the local authority Social Services Department visits the family to see if they require any kind of help.

All too frequently, however, the service fails at this initial point. One reason may be that schizophrenia often begins in the late teens or early twenties and this is a time when difficult and odd behaviour can occur in any case. Because of this, parents may be told rather briskly that they are worrying needlessly. However, having once been brushed off in this way, they are reluctant to approach their G.P. again, and often things have to get very bad indeed before they do so. One young patient, for example, had been very disturbed and had been smashing windows. His parents called the doctor. The patient was very suspicious and said 'What have you come for? What have you got in that bag?' The G.P. told the parents there was nothing he could do, as the patient did not appear to be an actual danger. He said he had other patients to attend to, and left hastily. Perhaps the G.P. did not see any role for himself in this situation but the parents were left without any form of help for their considerable difficulties. Parents who were themselves G.P.s said that they had known little about the illness before having personal experience of it, and they felt sure that, in general, the average G.P. had not had a great deal of experience of it.

Sometimes parents made their initial approach to the local Social Services Department as well as to the G.P. and, here again, their needs were frequently left unmet. One father told how he became worried at the odd way his son was behaving, and contacted the local Social Services Department. The impression this father gained from the Department was that 'they did not seem to want to know', and told him to contact his G.P. The G.P. was equally uninterested, and told him to contact the Social Services. This story was a typical one, and it illustrates the kind of breakdown which can occur right at the start. In this case nothing was done until the situation reached such a crisis that compulsory admission became necessary. In a similar instance, a mother saw that her son was becoming very disturbed, and approached her G.P. and her Social Services Department several times. She was treated brusquely and it was implied that her own stability was in question. Nothing was done and eventually the disaster which she had foreseen occurred, when the son committed a sexual assault and was finally compulsorily admitted to hospital.

These are fairly typical problems families described as occurring at the start of the illness, just when they were at their most bewildered and anxious and most in need of help. One mother said, 'You feel you must be making a fuss, because no one seems to see the problem, so you think well, I'd better just soldier on a bit longer'. Soldier on they do − but the result can be an all-out crisis resulting in an unnecessary compulsory hospital admission. This in itself is a traumatic event, the patient often feeling betrayed by his family and the family feeling guilty and unsure that they have done the right thing.

The need for initial information

Assuming, however, that initial obstacles have been overcome, and some contact with services has been established, what is needed next is guidance and support. Several relatives said that when the patient was first admitted to hospital, they felt bewildered and 'shell-shocked'. Many complained that they had turned to doctors or social workers for information but had received none. Some had not even been given any diagnosis but had found out indirectly for themselves (such as by seeing it written on the sickness certificate signed by the G.P.). Usually it came as a great shock, as relatives had heard the word 'schizophrenia' used vaguely in the same context as words like 'criminal' and 'psychopath'. One mother, horrified to hear the diagnosis, asked her son's psychiatrist for more information about the illness. He responded by saying, 'Oh, schizophrenia is something you will find in all walks of life. You get schizophrenic doctors, schizophrenic teachers − nothing unusual in that'. This mother was far from reassured by this lighthearted attitude, especially as she could see for herself how severely disturbed her son was. At the other extreme, however, many relatives had been told by doctors: 'There's no cure for this, he will never be any different'. These relatives felt the doctor had at any rate given them an honest opinion, but they felt defeated. Since the doctors appeared to have given up the case, they also felt hopeless about any possibility of improvement.

Some relatives, feeling the illness and its treatment lay

shrouded in clouds of mystery, would clutch at any straw which seemed to suggest a way out. They might invest undue hope in reports of miracle cures seen in the press. This is something which is likely to happen where relatives are kept in the dark and not given such knowledge as is available.

Hospital care

Several relatives were concerned about the care given in hospital. Where a patient had been in hospital for a long time, say more than a year, a few relatives complained about the physical care of the patient (dental care, for example, or treatment for minor physical ailments). Others spoke of the depressing atmosphere in the back wards of large, old, hospital buildings. Often, of course, the hospitals were modern, and the atmosphere less depressing than this. Also, the admission might well be a short one. This, too, could be a problem, as sometimes a patient under order would stay in the hospital only the statutory 28 days, and then would refuse to stay longer. If he was not ill enough to be kept in compulsorily·for a further period, he might go home whilst still in a somewhat disturbed state. Several relatives complained about this, feeling that the patient should have been prevented from discharging himself in this way. The situation was even worse when relatives were not informed about the patient's discharge.

In general, the main feeling about hospital care was that relatives were not included in the treatment plan and that their cooperation was not sought in spite of the fact that, as soon as the patient left hospital, they had to take responsibility.

Medication

Once a patient was discharged from hospital, there were sometimes problems in ensuring that he continued to take his medication. In 40 cases out of 65 in which medication had been prescribed, it was taken regularly. For 12 cases it was only taken infrequently and in three cases the patient refused altogether. Some relatives did not see regular medication as very important. As one put it, 'I leave all that to her. I would not know if she remembers to take it or not, I have enough to do without thinking about her tablets as well'. Others, however, were most concerned about it, and some parents felt very anxious that the

Table 13

Type of medication and side-effects mentioned

Type of medication:	Total (N = 80)	% of Total
Tablets	44	55
Injections (or injections & tablets)	26	33
None	7	4
Not known	3	4
Side effects:		
Overweight	20	25
Sleepiness	26	33
Other side effects (e.g. twitching, eyes rolling upwards)	14	18

patient would not remember to take his medication regularly when they were no longer there to give it to him.

A small group of patients had not recently been prescribed any medication. Some of these patients objected to medication, saying that drugs would destroy their minds and make them 'into vegetables'. Others had no clearly expressed objection of this kind and the lack of medication was rather a reflection of the fact that they had drifted out of touch with services, at times largely because relatives had become embittered with their experiences and had given up trying to get help from services.

In a very small number of cases, a visiting community psychiatric nurse from the local psychiatric hospital would visit regularly to give the patient an injection of fluphenazine. G.Ps could also be helpful in this respect. For example, a G.P. who saw the patient at regular intervals to give him an injection could, if the patient failed to turn up, call at the home and persuade the patient to have it. This kind of help was much appreciated by relatives.

Several relatives were worried about the possible side effects of long-term medication. A quarter of the patients were overweight and a slightly higher number suffered from drowsiness. It was not possible, of course, for relatives to judge how far such effects were attributable to the medication. It was mentioned above that many patients had a tendency to develop sudden odd physical complaints such as twitching, shaking, or involuntary rolling upwards of the eyes. It is difficult for relatives to know whether these are due to medication or not (usually they are) and they were not always given very precise advice about how to anticipate them and what to do.

Hospital aftercare: the need for advice and guidance

A number of relatives said that they had been left entirely without help when the patient first came out of hospital. They would have welcomed someone who could give guidance about how to cope with behaviour problems and advice about the kind of everyday set-up within which the patient might be able to function best. Instead they were often left to 'sink or swim' or to find out by trial and error how to cope with the problems of the illness.

Many relatives had tried to see the patient's psychiatrist to ask advice and had had great difficulty in achieving this. One, for example, had written and been given an appointment. She had taken time off from work (thus losing pay she could ill spare) and had gone to the hospital on the appointed day. However, when she arrived, she was told the psychiatrist was away on holiday. She made another appointment and on this second occasion (once again losing time from work) she saw him but 'he was in such a hurry I only had about five minutes with him'. In other cases, relatives had made an appointment to see the psychiatric social worker at the hospital, hoping for help and guidance. Instead, the social worker took a detailed social history of the patient and often this was the last the family saw of her.

The kind of advice relatives felt was needed would have covered the day to day problems of living with schizophrenia. For example, what was the best way to approach and communicate with the patient? Many relatives had found out over the years that a patient could not cope with too much emotional intrusion from them. 'I've found that he doesn't like too much demonstrative affection'; 'an indirect approach seems to work best'; 'if you criticise his behaviour directly, you get nowhere'. Finding out this kind of thing by trial and error was a painful and exhausting process and often relatives felt embittered that they had not received more guidance of this kind at the start of the illness.

Another sphere in which relatives often felt advice was needed concerned how far they should protect a patient from the ordinary knocks of everyday living. For example, if there were a younger sibling in the family who tended to tease the patient, how far should the parents exert their authority and stop this? Parents often felt that a younger child was not receiving all the attention he should, because of the patient's illness, and was having to 'grow up too quickly'. They therefore felt guilty about being strict with him, yet feared that the teasing would be more than the patient could stand. Similarly, relatives commonly wanted advice about how much they should expect of the patient; what standards of behaviour should they demand? One patient was discharged from hospital and simply spent all day lying on his bed, not washing or bothering to dress. His parents had no idea what they should do. They contacted the psychiatrist who told them to be permissive and let the son do as he pleased. The result was that he continued to deteriorate.

Many relatives discovered for themselves that patients were better when there was a certain amount of structure to their lives. They found that a consistent firmness, without excessive pressure, worked best. An outside person with some authority who was willing to help them in this was invaluable. This was particularly the case if there was a degree of conflict between the parents, or if only one parent was coping alone.

The need for genetic counselling and advice on family planning

The need to advise patients on matters of family planning was something which became apparent during the course of this investigation, although it was not specifically mentioned in the interview schedule. If the patient is herself a mother having difficulty in coping with her children, the matter of family planning should always be discussed. It is probable that many patients (particularly those lacking in initiative) will not seek such advice of their own accord. In some instances, a domiciliary visit would have been valuable, especially if the patient was fearful and self-conscious in social situations, and might be unwilling to attend a clinic.

Family planning advice is equally important for the single female patient. This is obviously true if there are signs of promiscuity, though this was not true of any of the patients in this investigation. However, in addition, a very passive patient could also be at risk of becoming pregnant, either through her naivety and excessively trusting attitude towards others, or through a lack of understanding of what sex is about. Another way in which contraception might be of value might be in reducing the painful or distressing side-effects of menstrual periods. A few relatives felt that relapses seemed to be associated with these.

Many relatives were concerned about the possibility of schizophrenia being an inherited complaint. Brothers or sisters of patients who wanted to have children were particularly worried about this. Genetic counsellors are now attached to some general hospitals and general practitioners can refer their patients to them for advice. However, very little skilled genetic counselling is available to schizophrenic patients and their relatives outside a few special clinics.

The role of social workers
If guidance and advice are to be offered, it seems that social workers might provide the service. Some families felt that a social worker ought to visit the home routinely after a patient had left hospital and particularly if he discharged himself against medical advice. On the occasions when this had occurred, relatives had found it a great help. Some families spoke highly of the service they had received, particularly when they had had the same social worker for several years and felt that there was someone they could rely upon and turn to in difficulty. Only a very small number of families had received visits from a community psychiatric nurse. This system seemed to work very well, as the nurses had seen the patient both in the hospital and the family, and gave helpful advice on management. Unfortunately follow-up services after hospital were rarely as good as this. Two main complaints were levelled against social workers by relatives. One was that they were unreliable; the other that they lacked understanding of relatives' problems. Complaints about reliability were quite frequent. Thus in one instance a social worker from the hospital visited a mother while her son was an inpatient. This social worker seemed very concerned and sympathetic and the mother felt confidence in her. She told the mother to telephone her if ever she had any problems. Later, when the son was discharged and began to become disturbed

again, the mother phoned this social worker several times to ask for help. But she did not manage to contact her, and though she left messages, she heard nothing further. This was by no means an isolated instance. Many relatives told of how a social worker had called once and promised help, and then had never been seen again. This made families feel very let down, having had their hopes raised that at last somebody in authority was sympathetic to their problems. 'I think the Welfare are paid for nothing', was one relative's bitter comment after relating such an incident.

The other major complaint was that social workers lacked understanding of the problems relatives faced. One mother, for instance, said she felt that the social worker did not really believe her when she said she was terrified of her son's rages. In the social worker's presence he was always rational and sensible and she seemed to feel that the mother was exaggerating and fussing over nothing. Another mother was very concerned about her son and was showing signs of breaking down under the strain. She approached the local social services department, but was only told 'not to worry' and to 'let him lead his own life'. Whatever the basis of this mother's fears, the lack of understanding of her real distress was hardly calculated to improve the situation. If the social services fail to appreciate the magnitude and complexity of such problems, one wonders where the relatives can turn for help. There seems to be a tendency to judge relatives as 'overanxious', or 'overprotective', and a lack of realisation that people in crisis do often become agitated and confused. They need all the support possible to cope with what one relative described as the 'discordance of living constantly with abnormality'.

Nevertheless, when a social worker was efficient, her intervention in a situation could make a major contribution. An example of such help occurred when a middle-aged patient, who had been hospitalised for over two years, suddenly discharged himself to his sister and brother-in-law's home. At the time this could have created a crisis, as both of these relatives were at work all day. However the social worker immediately arranged for the patient to attend a local day centre and no delay was involved. The social worker was on hand to discuss initial problems of the patient settling in to the home and the patient's sister knew where to contact her if she needed any further help. From time to time the social worker telephoned the sister to ask if all was well, and the situation appeared stable and fairly satisfactory for all concerned.

Practical help

The continuity of the situation is often the greatest problem. Once the patient is established living at home, the relatives caring for him may become tied to the house. One of the most frequent complaints was never being able to take a break from caring for the patient. However fond of him they were, the relatives naturally wished to have a holiday from time to time. 'If only my husband and I could just have one week away alone together, I feel we could cope so much better when we came back'. Although a few families were able to arrange short-term care, it was usually only in those cases where the patient was stable in behaviour and where a capable and sympathetic relative was willing to step into the parents' shoes while they were away. Some parents said they would be glad of an exchange scheme, whereby they could care for another couple's son or daughter while that couple had a holiday and then reverse the arrangement.

Some relatives felt that they could not leave the patient alone even for an evening. This was particularly the case if he was inclined to 'wander off' at night. These relatives wished there were some kind of 'sitter' arrangement, for example, for a mother on her own, who could become extremely lonely and isolated through being tied constantly to the house. The need for an 'evening off' arrangement for relatives should not be underestimated. Being continually bound by the dependence of a patient can lead to resentment on the relatives' part and a generally tense atmosphere in the household. This in turn can lead to a deterioration in the patient's behaviour and so a vicious circle is established.

Practical help of a specialised kind is also needed where the patient is a mother with young children. One mother had regular 'off days', when for a few days she would sit slumped in a chair and was incapable of doing anything at all. Some sort of 'on call' home help service would seem appropriate here. Otherwise it is likely to be the father, if he is still around, who has to step in. But if this kind of thing occurs regularly his work is likely to suffer seriously. He will also be exhausted by caring for the children, as well as coping with his wife's illness and trying to keep his job. The whole family situation becomes likely to break down.

Hostel provision

Most relatives felt that they had sufficient living space available. In most cases, the patient had a room and the housing amenities were adequate.

While some relatives felt that they could cope if they could have occasional breaks from caring for the patient, many others felt that a hostel providing a supportive environment where the patient could live independently of them would be the right solution. Older parents who feared what would happen to the patient when they were no longer able to care for him felt this particularly.

Several patients had been in a hostel at some time in the past, but these had generally been designed to help the individual to become independent enough to live in the community. Parents felt this aim was often unrealistic and that many patients might also need a sheltered environment for the rest of their lives. In fact the role such hostels had played had often been to give the parents an extended break rather than to rehabilitate the patient so that he was able to live independently of his relatives. This role in itself was valuable but regrettably short-term. As one mother put it, 'wherever he goes, and whichever authority takes an interest in him, in the end, after they've done what they can for him, it's all back on my plate again'.

Financial problems

About one-third of families faced difficulties over problems of money. One problem is that the scheme of sickness and unemployment benefits is designed to cater for people who live at a permanent address and are temporarily out of work or sick. Patients suffering from schizophrenia often move about a great deal, take jobs they are too ill to manage, and then give them up after a few days or weeks. The patient is then not eligible for unemployment pay because he has left the job of his own accord. However, he is no longer eligible for sick pay either, without going through the whole process of application again, since he has been in employment. He could claim Supplementary Benefit, but arranging this quickly is notoriously difficult. If he has no permanent address it is even harder. Patients often took one look at all the questioning and form-filling which was required, and gave up.

Many relatives had taken over this side of things completely. A few patients would go every week to the labour exchange and sign on to obtain unemployment pay. But most found this weekly encounter with officialdom too much. Many parents had struggled their way through the system so many times on the patient's behalf that they knew how to work it. Even so there could be sudden unexpected disruption just when relatives thought that the finances, at least, had been sorted out. One mother whose son had been on sick benefit for some time suddenly received a notice for him to attend for DHSS medical examination. He did so, was pronounced fit for work, and his benefit instantly stopped. Fortunately, in this case, a sympathetic G.P. stepped in and sorted matters out. This patient was fortunate in having relatives to fight for him and a general practitioner to support them.

One of the most satisfactory financial arrangements was for the patient to receive sickness benefit by obtaining a three-monthly certificate from the G.P. The number of patients who were supported by sickness benefit was very small, however; about one-fifth. A different set of problems arose when a patient refused to claim benefit. With supplementary benefit, for example, relatives can make many of the arrangements, but a visitor from the Department of Health had to call and see the claimant before payments could be started. If the patient has objections to claiming benefit there is little relatives can do and this could mean financial hardship if he is dependent upon them. The problem did not show up a great deal in this investigation. Most of those with no income were housewives supported by their husbands. One patient lived with relatives who felt that all forms of state benefit were 'charity' and it was by their own choice that no claim was made. Only one patient refused to claim though his relatives would have liked him to have done so. However, it seems probable that the problem is in fact much greater than this study suggests. Camberwell has better services than average and benefits were arranged where necessary. The

Fellowship group was composed of relatives who were, on the whole, aware of their rights, articulate and determined. Thus both groups of patients had competent people to see to the arranging of their financial support. If the initial arrangements are made efficiently the benefit is continued automatically without any further effort on the patient's part. Many relatives nevertheless mentioned problems at the beginning when they had first tried to arrange financial benefits for the patient. These relatives did not give up easily, but had the patient been alone in the world or had the relatives been less capable in coping with officialdom, it seems likely that nothing further would have been done. Patients who are not in touch with services or with their families seem highly liable to become destitute. Without any income at all, they could then become dragged down by a whole host of secondary problems.

Another difficulty which sometimes arose was when a patient had no idea of the value of money. Some did not bother to cash their giros or lost them. Others might spend all their money at once on things they had no need of. Relatives who tried to arrange for the giros to be sent to them instead, found this required a very long and complicated process. This is obviously designed to prevent abuse, but also prevents use.

Another financial problem mentioned was finding the money for the prescriptions for a patient's long-term medication. Although persons suffering from schizophrenia must take preventive medication, they are not eligible for exemption from prescription charges. This became quite expensive when a patient had a number of different types of tablet. Some relatives had bought a 'season ticket' to reduce this expenditure but then found that if the patient was readmitted to hospital during the period covered by the season ticket, the money spent on it was not refundable.

It is the unpredictability of the patient with schizophrenia, his tendency to move from place to place, from a job to unemployment and then on to another job, that makes him likely to slip through the social security net. His ability to tolerate form-filling and the accompanying investigations into his eligibility for benefit, is lower than average. The patient sometimes prefers to go without, and this may mean that his relatives have to provide for him, and go without themselves.

The need for occupation

One very important problem which relatives frequently mentioned was how to occupy the patient during the day. This is a crucial issue. For one thing, patients show less deterioration when they have something to do for a good part of the day. Equally important, it gives relatives and the patient a break from each other which is beneficial to all concerned.

If the patient was able to manage it, a job was the ideal solution. However, the fact that alternative forms of occupation (such as day centres) were rarely available, meant that sometimes relatives exerted pressure on a patient to get a job even though he really was not capable of it. It was an understandable reaction on their part, since they could see he was deteriorating through having nothing to do and the atmosphere in the household was becoming increasingly tense. However, helping a patient to readjust to work is a complex operation. Some relatives complained that they had had little help from the Disablement Resettlement Officer at the local Employment Exchange although they had hoped these officers would be able to help with placing the patient in a job. Some relatives had heard of Industrial Rehabilitation Units. At these Units, assessment of the capabilities of people who have been unemployed for some time through sickness or disablement is carried out and suitable training recommended. However, some relatives had been unable to obtain a place for the patient at an Industrial Rehabilitation Unit. Even when they had managed this, other breakdowns in the service sometimes nullified the benefit an IRU course could provide. Some patients, for example, made a great effort to do well on an IRU course. Yet having successfully completed it, Disablement Resettlement Officers at the local labour exchanges were unable to find them jobs. Thus all the effort expended in getting them back into work and assessing their capabilities went to waste. The effect on the patient was usually considerable, and he became very discouraged and embittered after having built up his hopes of returning to work. One young patient did extremely well on the clerical side at an IRU and was offered further training at an office work course in a nearby town. This involved a lot of travelling, and would have meant catching a train at 7.00 in the morning and not getting home until 6.30 in the evening. The patient's parents therefore asked the DRO if there was any chance of arranging local accommodation during the week. The DRO promised this would be done. The parents telephoned several times to check about this, while waiting for the vacancy on the course, and each time were told all was well. A few days before it began, having heard nothing further about accommodation, they phoned again, and were told that the DRO they had been dealing with had left, and the present one knew nothing of the promises made previously. If the patient could not cope with the long day, then he would have to forfeit his place on the course. Having no alternative, he did in fact make every effort. But he became exhausted by the travelling and eventually gave up the course. This patient had worked hard both at the IRU and on the subsequent clerical course, and given proof of his ability. It seems wasteful and unnecessary that he should have been left unemployed.

It is true that patients are often very difficult to place in jobs, and probably they are sometimes refused places at IRU's to avoid this kind of disappointment. Also they often fail to stay the course. This may sometimes be because Units are not entirely suited to the special needs of the patient suffering from schizophrenia. For example, one highly intelligent young man, whose interests had always been of an academic nature, relapsed after one day at an IRU where he had to do manual work. He had never done work of this kind before and it could perhaps have been predicted that he would be unable to cope. Too often there seemed to be a lack of careful planning, so that the potential value of the time spent on an IRU course went to waste. Much of what relatives said seemed to echo the findings of a previous study, that unless services are well co-ordinated, and the IRU course is part of a well organised long-term plan for the patient, it will have little effect on subsequent employment history.

The patients who were working were in the minority, and they were often encountering problems at work. They were often, for example, hypersensitive to criticism, so that if a patient was unlucky enough to have an unsympathetic supervisor in his job, he might become very disturbed. It is the kind of thing which can happen to anyone in any job, but with these patients, the difficulties inherent in such situations became magnified in intensity. Often a patient would simply throw up a job over something like this rather than trying to reach a solution. His family might remain completely in the dark as to the reason for his leaving.

Another problem with working patients was that they could be 'put upon' by other workers. This was perhaps because patients were often easy to take advantage of and could not stand up for themselves. Some relatives mentioned occasions when this had happened and they had been able to talk with the patient's employer so that things could be sorted out.

Particular problems arise with more intelligent patients. Often they had had to take a job considerably below their ability, because the pressures and the responsibilities of a more demanding job were more than they could take. This did not stop them from feeling frustrated with the lack of opportunity to use their intelligence. In this sense they were, in many ways, worse off than less intelligent patients.

Nearly all the patients with jobs were having difficulties at work. The actual number was small, since most patients had been unemployed for more than 5 years. The more pressing problem, therefore, was what to do during the daytime. About one quarter of the Camberwell patients attended a day centre, but very few of the Fellowship patients were able to do so. Patients who have no form of occupation in the day have a high risk of relapsing, particularly if they spend much of the day in face-to-face contact with a relative who is critical. Many relatives said they wished the patient could attend a day centre. Some had tried to arrange this but had been told there was no such centre in their area. For such relatives there was no relief. As one put it: 'It's having to be with him 24 hours a day that's such a strain. It's like having a small child around you all the time and at my age I feel I need a rest from that'.

Where a patient was receiving some form of day care, relatives were generally well satisfied and felt it made a great difference to the whole household. However, problems could arise even so. For example, the more intelligent patient might find the kind of work provided at a day centre too boring and repetitive. Sometimes a patient would suddenly refuse to go to a day centre after having been apparently settled. In such a case, it is important that there should be someone who can liaise between family and day centre to try and find out what has gone wrong and whether it can be put right. All too often, however, there was nobody and so once again a patient reverted to remaining at home and unoccupied all day.

Illustrative Case Histories

The following five case-histories have been chosen to illustrate how the problems described in this report, and the methods used by relatives and helping agencies to overcome them, were actually experienced by families. Two of the patients live in Camberwell; in one case the present arrangements are reasonably satisfactory, in the other they leave a good deal to be desired. The other three patients are from the Fellowship's list and illustrate a range of situations, from one in which the family has compensated fairly well to one in which there are still very severe and unresolved problems.

Details about the families have been disguised so that none of the people concerned can be identified.

Geoffrey

Geoffrey S. was a married man in his mid-forties. His illness had started in his early twenties and he had at one time been an in-patient for 17 years. His wife, who was interviewed, was most scathing about the treatment he received during that time and said 'they just used to leave them sitting on the Ward like vegetables'. Since this first very long admission, Mr. S. had had one short admission of a few weeks and one longer one lasting a year. He had been discharged from this last admission 15 months prior to the interview.

Since his discharge Mr. S. had been attending a local Day Centre regularly and seemed to be happy there. His wife said that he had improved markedly over the 15 months. He was much less withdrawn than he had been. 'There was a time when you could sit in the room with him for hours on end and he wouldn't say a word. But now if anything's worrying him or upsetting him he'll always tell me'. Mr. S. now took a keen interest in football and always watched the matches on T.V. remembering all the scores of the different games he had seen. He also helped a great deal around the house and Mrs. S.

said in a gratified tone, 'I never have to wash a dish'.

Mrs. S. managed a small shop and the two of them lived above it. Their children were grown up and married. Mrs. S. gave a very sensible and competent impression. She did not seem at all concerned at being the breadwinner of the household and was somewhat puzzled when asked if there had been any recent financial worries connected with her husband's illness. 'Well no', she said, 'I've always gone to work even when the children were small and I manage'. What Mr. S. earned at the Day Centre was only sufficient to cover his fares and to pay for his lunch there, but Mrs. S. did not want him to take a job. 'I'd rather he stayed as he is', she said, 'he's so much better since he's been going to the Day Centre. I'd far rather he stayed there than try and do a job and end up back at square one'.

Mrs. S. said that her health was unaffected by Mr. S's illness. 'You can't let it be affected' she said. She did say she felt a little overtired at times, but this was because she worked long hours and did not have a complete day off at all in the week. Objectively she appeared to have had a very hard life. For 17 years while her children were growing up she had had to be both mother and breadwinner. She showed no resentment of this. Her view was that her husband had been very ill and needed her all the more because of this. She was a fairly forceful person of a warm but 'no nonsense' disposition, and seemed very prepared to fight for her husband's rights.

Mrs. S. expressed herself fully satisfied with the help she was receiving from services. Her husband attended a local out-patient clinic every few weeks and received an injection of fluphenazine. Mrs. S. knew how to contact the doctor there if she had any difficulties and was also in contact with a local authority social worker in whom she expressed a great deal of confidence. She knew the supervisor at the Day Centre too, and felt she could rely upon her. 'She'd always let me know if she was at all worried about Geoffrey and I'd always let *her* know if I had any problem'.

A large part of the success of this programme could be attributed to Mrs. S's personality. She said that she had herself initiated her husband's discharge after 17 years and claimed she had met opposition from the medical staff – 'I really had to fight to get him out of there'. She had a great deal of drive and an ability to put her case clearly which probably helped her to obtain the full benefit of services. Mrs. S. also had a fairly low expectation of what life can offer. She was content to spend long hours working hard and accepted this as just being the way things had turned out. She was fortunate in that she lived in an area served by a Day Centre, and that the supervisor took such an interest in the relatives of those who attended. She was also fortunate in having a social worker upon whom she could rely. Communications between the services, and between herself and the services, were good, and the situation appeared stable.

Victoria

Victoria C. was a Nigerian lady in her mid-twenties, married with 4 children, between one and eight years old. She had first become ill 6 years previously after coming to England. She had had 4 admissions, all of them short. Her husband who was interviewed described how on the most recent occasion he had come home from work to find his wife in a very disturbed state saying that the neighbours were plotting against her. It was a shock to him, as she had shown no sign of disturbance when he had left for work that morning. He saw that he would have to take her to hospital, so tried to persuade her to go with him to where his car was parked. At first she seemed willing to do so, but then began to struggle with him on the very public walkway of the block of council flats where they lived. She began to call out to neighbours that her husband was trying to kill her. Her husband said that he still felt embarrassed with the neighbours over this incident and was sure they thought that he ill-treated his wife.

He eventually managed to get her to hospital where she was admitted and where he saw a social worker to ask what could be done about the two under-school-age children. The social worker sent Mr. C. to his local area Social Service office. There he was told that somebody would call on him. He returned home to the children. Nobody came from the Social Services until 2 days had passed. During this time the baby would not stop crying day or night and Mr. C. said he 'went through hell'. After the social worker had called, it was a further 2 days before Mr. C. was informed that a foster home had been found. He then had to drive the baby and the four-year-old child some considerable distance to the home. He said the drive was terrible as the baby would not stop crying and the other child was also rather disturbed and kept climbing over the seats.

After her discharge, Mrs. C. had not always been well. Every 4 or 5 weeks she would have a few days when she seemed incapable of doing anything. At these times she would just sit in the chair, would not eat, and did not bother to wash. Mr. C. had to take time off work whenever this happened and this meant that he lost pay. In fact his career prospects had been seriously affected because of the illness. He had been taking post-graduate training for a professional job, but had had to interrupt the course so frequently that he eventually had to give it up and was now working for London Transport. Money was tight and the family was in some debt. Social life was also affected, as Mr. C. said he was a gregarious person but found his wife did not like to mix socially outside the home.

The strain upon the marriage was severe but Mr. C. said he would not leave his wife because he believed marriage should be for life. In any case he felt that a breakup would not solve anything because of the children: 'They are already born'. He felt that his wife's 'spells' had a serious enough effect upon the children as it was. One child in particular became very distressed and tearful when Mrs. C. was not well. Whilst he appeared stoical and fully prepared to accept his responsibilities, Mr. C. did say he wished now he had never married. He did not however blame his wife for the way things had turned out. When asked whether he felt she could do more to help herself, he said 'You might as well say to a pilot in an aeroplane whose engine suddenly fails, "Can't you do something to help yourself?" He cannot however he tries'.

Mr. C. said that different social workers called from time to time. He did not see that they could help him in any way, except by arranging care of the children promptly in an emergency. He thought that if one social worker was to visit his wife regularly this might help her to remain more stable, but he was not sure about this as his wife generally did not like talking to people. He was vague about his wife's medication. He knew she had tablets, but did not know whether or not she took them regularly. However, he was disturbed by the fact that she had put on a great deal of weight since she had been taking them which he did not like. He had spoken to her doctor about this but had the impression that nothing could be done.

This family was apparently undergoing a lot of strain because of Mrs. C's illness. Mrs. C. probably found the effort of coping with four young children was too much, especially in a country where she was a relative stranger. The outlook here was not a good one, especially if Mrs. C. had more children, and continued to relapse at intervals. Mrs. C. was fortunate in having a husband who was intelligent and competent. He was rather puzzled at the inefficiency of the emergency social work service, saying 'I thought it was an official thing — to do with the Government — is this not correct?' It seemed likely that Mr. C's strong sense of duty to his family would mean he would remain with them, and that he would become more skilled at getting better service from agencies as time went on. However, the effect upon the family's general standard of living and upon the development of the children gives great cause for concern.

Phillip

Phillip K. was in his mid-thirties and lived with his parents who were well-to-do professional people. His illness had begun during his early twenties. He had always been rather shy and diffident even as a child, though he was academically good at school. He obtained a University Degree though he had to take a term off during the course because things were getting on top of him. After this he tried to obtain a professional qualification, and it was during this time that he was first admitted to a psychiatric hospital.

Phillip returned home from this first admission to live with his parents. As he had been admitted to a hospital in a different part of the country from that in which they lived, his parents had no communication with the staff there and had little idea of what had been the matter with their son. They assumed he must be 'cured' of whatever it was, but were disturbed to notice a change in his personality. He seemed offhand in manner, inconsiderate and rather rude in all kinds of ways, and this was in marked contrast to his usual behaviour. He began to act very oddly and started to be antagonistic towards his parents. Eventually he disappeared. His parents by now were extremely anxious. Fortunately they had a friend who was a doctor (though not their

G.P.). He advised them that they had good grounds for anxiety, and ought to make every effort to trace Phillip. This they did and finally managed to find him dirty and unkempt in a seedy London hotel. They took him home and he was once again admitted to hospital.

During this admission, Phillip's father made a point of arranging an interview with Phillip's doctor and was given the diagnosis. When Phillip was discharged, his father requested some form of after-care but the doctor said this was unnecessary and that Phillip would be all right as long as he took his tablets regularly. His parents took this to mean that they should simply remind Phillip about his pills each day and this they did. It was a long time later that they learned he had not in fact been taking them. During the next few years Phillip tried different jobs but was never able to stick to any for long. Whenever he was living at home he acted strangely, staying out at night for example (though his parents did not know where he went for he did not appear to have any social life) and sometimes expressing odd ideas.

After several years of this, a social contact of Phillip's mother, who knew something of psychiatric services in the area, suggested that Phillip might be willing to attend a day hospital of which she had a high opinion. This was duly arranged and proved to be a turning point for Phillip. The doctor there was struck by how difficult it was to get through to him, his only reply to questions being 'Oh, yes, yes, sorry', otherwise not responding in any way. He had taken no medicine since the earlier second admission to hospital: the doctor suggested to his parents that they might persuade him to take chlorpromazine (Largactil) regularly. This was achieved by his mother saying in a purposely casual way 'Well, your father and brother take various pills, what about trying this one, the doctor thinks it will do you good, it's got some vitamins in'. So this he did and it resulted in an immediate and dramatic change, and for the first time he was calm and even sat down to watch T.V. remarking 'I feel a bit sleepy'. This change was maintained. Though some adjustment of dosage was necessary in the early stages, once fixed no further alteration has been needed. He did very well at the day hospital and after some time was moved to a hostel some distance away from which he could travel each day to a sheltered workshop.

Each weekend he came home from the hostel and his parents were delighted at how greatly his condition had improved. After almost a year of this, Phillip said he now felt ready to live at home and do a job. This was arranged, and the local Labour Exchange was most helpful in finding him work as a Disabled Person with a local firm.

At the time of the interview for this study Phillip had been working at the firm for four years. He still had various residual handicaps such as neglecting his appearance somewhat or sitting laughing to himself. These oddities were accepted by the people he worked with and by his family. His parents found he would usually control his strange mannerisms if he was at a social gathering with people outside the family, and if he forgot to do so, he could be reminded by a frown or a shake of the head. He had developed an interest in various hobbies over the last couple of years and his parents were delighted by this as they remembered a time when he had taken no interest in anything at all. The main problem was that he periodically became obsessed with certain delusional ideas, believing, for example, that he and his parents were being poisoned. His parents had tried several ways of coping with this and now used a warm but not over-sympathetic approach, saying for example, 'Oh dear, it *is* a nuisance isn't it. I am sorry you're upset again'. They were fortunate in having a helpful G.P. who would visit Phillip when he was very distressed by these ideas, talk to him about it and usually give him some medicine. Phillip would have a day or two off from work, and would then once again be well for a period.

This case illustrates well how a patient can be contained within the community. It is of interest to note, however, that Phillip's first referral to the rehabilitation services he needed came about by pure chance, through a social contact of his mother's. Once this referral had occurred, however, he received excellent help from services. Now that Phillip was living at home, his parents were fully satisfied with the help they received from the Labour Exchange. If ever Phillip had any difficulties at work they would ring the Exchange and found they could rely upon them to sort out the problem. The G.P. was also helpful and understanding whenever Phillip's delusional ideas threatened to distress him excessively. Phillip's parents said that they had found they felt much less overwhelmed and much more able to cope once they had lowered their expectations of Phillip. 'The great thing', they said, 'is to stop hoping for a cure or a job at the previous level of ability'. They also found Phillip was easier to manage now that he accepted himself as ill. This meant he was most careful to take his medication regularly. They felt rather worried about the future at times, and how Phillip would get on when they were no longer there to care for him. Although they could provide for him financially they were concerned at the lack of provision for a sheltered home environment within which patients like Phillip could live happily.

Mary

Mary T. was 18 years old at the time of the interview for this study. She lived with her parents and her younger brother and sister in a pleasant and comfortable three-bedroomed house in a Midlands town. Mary's mother, a warm, sympathetic person, clearly very concerned about her, described how Mary had first begun to act strangely when she was about 15. She was still at school at that time, although not doing very well as she was a slow learner and inclined to be shy. The first signs that something was amiss came when Mary became unusually silent and often seemed confused and muddled about simple matters. 'We couldn't understand what was the matter and why she was acting so silly', her mother said, but they had decided to discuss the problem with the family doctor. He attempted to dismiss their fears, saying 'Oh, teenage troubles are nothing unusual. She'll grow out of it'. However, Mary's parents persisted and eventually the G.P. agreed somewhat reluctantly to refer Mary to a psychiatrist.

The psychiatric appointment was made for several weeks ahead, but during the waiting period a crisis occurred. One morning Mary was found sitting on her bed 'like a pudding — like someone in a stupor'. She did not know her mother and stared at her vacantly saying, 'who are you?'. She had to be fed by hand and taken to the lavatory by her mother. Mary's parents were very frightened by all this. Her mother went to see the G.P. and he said that there was no need for him to visit as a psychiatric appointment had been made and he would try to make it an urgent one. They therefore telephoned the local psychiatric hospital. The staff were sympathetic but said the G.P. must be contacted first. This was done which annoyed the G.P. as he felt that Mary's parents had gone over his head by telephoning the hospital. However, immediately he saw her arrangements were started for her admission to the local adolescent unit.

It was several weeks before Mary knew her parents again. She attended the unit as an in-patient and then as a day-patient, for about a year. After her discharge Mary continued to have out-patient appointments at the local psychiatric unit. Her doctor there arranged for her to attend an Industrial Rehabilitation Unit. Unfortunately this meant Mary had to get up at 6.30 a.m. each morning in order to clock in at 8.00 a.m. She was becoming very overtired and also felt rather 'the odd one out' at the IRU because most of the others there were physically disabled. Several experimental changes were being made in the medication at this time and these had an adverse effect. It was suggested that Mary should leave the course and transfer to an industrial therapy unit which was attached to the local psychiatric hospital. She was also started on regular injections of fluphenazine.

Mary attended the unit daily from home for a year before she relapsed again. Shortly before this relapse Mary had been complaining about how much she hated the ITU, that the work was boring and repetitive, and that she wanted to do a 'proper job'. There had also been a lot of friction at home between her and her sister (eight years her junior). They quarrelled frequently and Mary had struck out at her sister from time to time. On this occasion Mary had relapsed with florid symptoms, becoming very overactive and aggressive.

When the interview for this study took place, Mary was again at home attending the ITU daily. Whilst her mother was pleased that Mary had some occupation in the day, there were several aspects of Mary's situation which caused her anxiety. Mary's mother felt some attempt should be made to place Mary in a job. She knew Mary could not cope with much stress, but felt there must be some kind of work she could do. As her younger brother would be going to college soon, Mary's mother felt Mary would feel more acutely than before that she was 'different' from other young people.

There were many aspects of Mary's illness which puzzled and worried her mother. For example, Mary spent most of the weekend in a deep 'almost unconscious' sleep. Her mother was anxious about this. Mary was physically aggressive at times and this was difficult to handle. Then there was the fact that Mary was 'always asking silly questions. Sometimes I think she must be acting so dim on purpose ... when she says she doesn't even know how to stitch up a hole in her tights and silly things like that'. Because of Mary's 'dimness' her mother also feared somebody might exploit her sexually. Although she had tried to explain something about sex, Mary seemed unable to understand. Her mother's worries on this score had increased when Mary had related how one of the men she knew at the ITU had tried to assault her sexually.

But there seemed to be nobody with whom Mary's mother could discuss these problems. Mary's parents had not seen her psychiatrist for two and a half years. They had recently written to ask for an appointment. This was not given, but a social worker called to see Mary's mother. She had explained some of the problems to the social worker, who said she would take them up with the doctor and call again. Three months later, however, nothing more had been heard.

This case is of interest because in many respects Mary was receiving a good service, but there were certain serious gaps in it. Whilst Mary was occupied during the day and was receiving regular medication, her home life did not seem to be included in the overall treatment plan. Mary's mother was anxious not to cause any bother, and felt reluctant to trouble Mary's doctor. Despite this, she also felt strongly that Mary had been 'forgotten' and that nobody took a personal interest in her. She feared that 'they' had decided Mary could never do a job and would spend the rest of her life going to the ITU. Problems of managing Mary's behaviour at home and the parents' need for more information and guidance were not being adequately met by services.

Michael

Michael D. was twenty-one years old at the time of the interview. Up to about the age of sixteen he had done well at school and showed a good deal of academic promise. However, after his 'O' level year he became involved with a group who were experimenting with drugs and his behaviour became very odd. He would not go back to school when a new term began, then he disappeared for a fortnight. When he returned his parents were seriously anxious about him. They felt that Michael was ill and arranged for him to see a psychiatrist as a private patient. This Michael did, but after the initial interview he refused to go again.

Michael lived at home during the following year and gradually got worse. He now complained frequently of hearing voices. At last his parents felt there was no alternative but to have him admitted to hospital. A compulsory admission was arranged through the G.P. His parents liked the hospital to which Michael was admitted and his mother saw the psychiatric social worker there regularly and found it helpful to discuss her anxieties about Michael with somebody sympathetic. However, after a few months Michael discharged himself. Once again living at home without a job he gradually deteriorated. The social worker still saw his mother but it seems no attempts were made to devise any form of rehabilitation programme for Michael. After several months Michael's symptoms became so bad that his mother enquired about the possibilities of readmission. She was told that Michael seemed to need long-term care and would therefore have to go to the local long-stay psychiatric hospital instead of the short-stay one where he had been before.

The admission was duly arranged but Michael's parents were appalled when they saw the ward he was in. It was very large, all men, gloomy and depressing. They felt that it was 'the end of the road' for him. It was not long before Michael discharged himself, and because his parents did not feel they could send him back to such a place he remained at home.

At the time of the interview for this study, Michael had been at home for over a year. He was not at all well and appeared to be getting worse, for example he had taken an interest in going to football matches with his father up to six months ago, but no longer did so. He neglected his appearance, was overactive and often laughed out loud for no apparent reason. He spent a large part of the day doing nothing at all, and every so often he simply disappeared for several days at a time. His mother felt that she was being seriously affected by all this and spoke of the strain of being constantly with him and having to cope with his strange behaviour. A further negative factor in the situation was that

Michael's younger sister had recently left home for college and because Michael's father worked long hours this meant that Michael and his mother spent a great deal of time alone together in the house (although they were not in face-to-face contact during all that time, as Michael spent quite a large part of the day alone in his room).

Michael was not having any help from services at the time of the interview and was not even receiving medication. When this had been arranged in the past Michael had always refused it after a short period. His father felt particularly bitter about this, as he said the doctors ought to have been firmer with Michael and insisted upon him taking the prescribed medication. Both parents felt very dissatisfied with services and felt that they had been left with the choice of either condemning Michael to a back-ward for the rest of his life, or having to accept the almost intolerable strains of living with him at home. They had decided that the only humane course was to accept the latter choice, despite the fact that, as his father put it 'it means you can never be free again'.

There had clearly been a failure in rehabilitative services here. As Michael's mother had been in regular contact with a hospital social worker over several months of the illness, this failure is particularly curious. It does seem that in some sense Michael had been 'given up'. Certainly the message that nothing more could be done had come over strongly to his parents who were now struggling entirely alone. This was by no means an untypical case although it was extreme in that there had been such a total cut-off from services. It does indicate that new knowledge of the management of schizophrenia, and ways in which an improvement in the patient's condition can be achieved, has not yet filtered through to many of the agencies dispensing medical and social services.

Discussion

Ideal and Reality
It may appear that this report has unduly emphasised the dark side of 'community care'. To some extent this is inevitable since we set out to obtain from the relatives a plain, unvarnished account of the problems entailed by living with schizophrenia.

Enlightened opinion in this country has moved steadily towards the view that handicapped children and adults should, as far as possible, live normal lives. There should be no discrimination on account of disability and every effort should be made to avoid segregation in isolated communities. The corollary is that the problems of handicap must be shared by the public in general; by neighbours, friends and workmates of handicapped people in particular, and above all by the close relatives who live with them and share their hopes, successes, crises and disappointments. Ideally, public attitudes would be such that a condition such as schizophrenia would constitute no stigma and public services would be so well developed that emotional, domestic, occupational and practical burdens would be rapidly, efficiently and sympathetically shared, and removed in so far as this is possible. We knew, before we started the survey, that 'community care' was still only an ideal and that public and private attitudes, and the provision of services, were nowhere adequate to meet the needs of handicapped people and their relatives. The deficiences are probably greatest when psychiatric disabilities, particularly schizophrenia, are involved. To some extent, therefore, this report must inevitably appear gloomy.

Nevertheless, there are bright features which deserve emphasis since they are often overlooked. We did *not* find, for example, that relatives in general were tetchy and complaining. On the contrary, most were tolerant and accepting in the face of problems that most people would find distressing and many would regard as insupportable. In many cases, relatives and patients had discovered for themselves how best to limit handicaps, promote assets and achieve a mode of life which had its pleasures and rewards as well as its disappointments. Such examples of positive 'coping' suggest that the principles involved can be described and adapted for more general use. Moreover, most people did have *some* experience of successful coping. Services were not uniformly bad. Everyone could think of individual professional people whose help was invaluable and specific situations in which a particular service performed its functions quickly, effectively and humanely. What was lacking was the maintenance of a uniformly high standard, with close co-ordination between different branches of a service. Another sizeable problem was that services that *were* available were not always used to greatest advantage. It is worthwhile considering this point at greater length.

Why do relatives not complain more?

It has never been the tradition in this country for services to be over-intrusive. The services are there and the assumption is that those in need will seek them out and ask for help. This is why, if a relative goes to his family doctor with his anxieties about a patient, he will often be told that nothing can be done unless the patient himself requests help, or unless he is so ill that he constitutes a definite danger to himself or to others. However, between the patient who defines himself as being in need of treatment and the patient who is so defined by the relevant authorities there lies a wide area of need which is ill-defined and not easy to assess. The problem is one of how the relevant services are to gain knowledge of this 'hidden' need, and of how they are then to meet it while at the same time ensuring that individual liberty is preserved.

The first difficulty here is that one cannot assume that those who need help will seek it. It is not only the patients who are unaware in any definite way of their need. At times relatives seemed to have become so used to a problem that they no longer regarded it as anything other than a normal part of everyday life. This was quite a different state of affairs from that pertaining where relatives had found a method of coping with a problem constructively. One young girl, for example, who lived alone with her mother (the patient) said, 'I never knew I was depressed until I was able to get away for a fortnight and I went abroad on holiday with a friend. It was only after I'd been away a few days that I suddenly realised how lighthearted I felt. It was such a contrast to how I normally feel'. She added that she would have denied any problem of depression had the question been asked of her before she had this experience. In another instance, a mother was asked whether her son had been threatening or violent. She replied vaguely, 'Oh no ... not really'. Questioned further, however, she said, 'Oh well, he punches me you know ... but I think everyone does that don't they?'. Whilst she appeared to be quite frightened of her son (and no doubt with good reason) she did not seem to see his violence as anything to complain about. Living constantly with disturbed behaviour may eventually alter relatives' ideas about what is 'normal'. This is not to say that their ability to tolerate such behaviour increases. They may still continue to feel depressed or anxious, but without attributing this to the patient. Instead they may come to regard the patient's difficult behaviour as a part of life which, although unpleasant, is unmodifiable and does not constitute grounds for complaint. Thus they do not see themselves as having a need and are not likely to be very demanding of services. If they do ask for help they will probably easily be put off or fall out of contact.

Sometimes the denial of a problem constitutes a method of dealing with it. One wife of a patient kept insisting she had no worries about her husband, that his illness was a thing of the past and would not recur. It was only when the interviewer got up to leave that this lady suddenly asked a number of questions in an anxious tone, such as how likely it was that her husband would be ill again, whether anyone was ever 'really cured' and where she could go to find a social worker in an emergency. No doubt this lady would present an appearance of having no need of information or advice if she was seen by a doctor or social worker. Any interview which took place at a service agency would probably of necessity be less thorough and probing than that used in this investigation. Because the lady's husband was not severely handicapped, and because she appeared competent and able to cope (as indeed she probably was) any less obvious needs would be liable to be overlooked.

Another reason why relatives might be less than demanding of services, was that some seemed to feel they were letting the patient down by discussing the difficulties encountered in living with him. One patient's sister, for example, said, 'I don't like saying anything about him — I feel like I'm betraying him. After all, blood is thicker than water. I wouldn't like them to say he had to go back into hospital'. Other relatives felt guilty at complaining and said, 'I'm painting a very black picture', or, 'Don't write that down. It makes him sound so awful'. Even when relatives found the patient's behaviour hard to tolerate, they sometimes felt to complain of it was in some sense to reject the patient.

So certain characteristics of relatives can result in their needs being left unmet. They do not always see that they have a need.

If they do perceive this they may feel they have no right to ask for help or may not know that there are services intended to meet their needs.

However, some relatives were aware of their rights, and articulate and determined in demanding assistance from services. Even so, they did not always get adequate assistance. Sometimes this may have been because of the 'front' presented to the service agency. It may be that if a relative appears aggressive, or over-anxious, or presents a vague and muddled picture of his difficulties, this confuses the issue so that the service agency fails to perceive the actual need that is there. Or sometimes social workers seemed to feel that the need had to be extreme before intervention was warranted. Relatives complained that if a compulsory admission was not regarded as essential, social workers seemed to have no further role to play. This is probably a function of the current shortage of staff in social services departments, the lack of workers experienced in the problems of schizophrenia and the excessive case-loads carried by many social workers. But it could also indicate poor planning of social work policy, and a lack of foresight, since today's problems and requests for help can be tomorrow's compulsory admissions. A few relatives, feeling that only emergencies received any attention from services, went so far as to create a 'false' crisis by pretending to wash their hands of the patient and claiming they would have no more to do with him. Such desperate measures did sometimes work, which indicates that our services are geared to coping with crises rather than to preventing them. However, such action was rather extreme and it is unlikely that the majority of relatives would feel happy about such an approach.

Another reason why services sometimes fail to respond appropriately to relatives' requests for help may lie in the complexity of the problems which can arise from schizophrenia. The problems are diffuse and may spread into several different areas of the patient's life, so that they are not easily categorised. This makes patients and relatives particularly vulnerable to gaps in communication between different services. Many agencies can be involved with the care of a schizophrenic patient in the community. Psychiatrists in out-patient clinics, the family doctor, social workers, the disablement resettlement officer, officers of the Department of Health and Social Security and workers from voluntary organisations might all be concerned in a particular case. Certain needs can pass unnoticed if co-ordination between the services is inadequate. The patients themselves are not likely to take the initiative in asking for help or in pointing out that there has been some omission in meeting a particular need. In fact patients will often react to a confusing or non-clear-cut situation by withdrawal. If the various helping agencies are not working together in a comprehensive programme designed to meet the patient's requirements, then the result can be that the patient falls out of contact with the network of services altogether. This can be avoided by somebody (often the social worker) acting as 'key worker', ensuring that the patient utilises all the services he requires and helping him with daunting procedures such as form-filling.

Discussing a study of schizophrenic patients and their relatives carried out in 1962, Brown and his colleagues wrote: 'We had the impression that relatives understated their problems. In part this was due to the fact that the intensity of problems fluctuated and people had rather short memories. If things were all right at the time the interviewer called, the whole of the previous five years seemed rosier. Another reason was that ... informants may have had many difficulties which they did not feel able to discuss. The most important factor, however, was probably that many relatives who lived with disabled patients subtly adapted their level of expectations so that, after a period of years, they no longer reacted according to their earlier hopes and ideals and perhaps had even forgotten them. ... Relatives are not in a strong position to complain: they are not experts, they may be ashamed to talk about their problems and they may have come to the conclusion that no help can be offered which will substantially reduce their difficulties. No "consumer" association exists which can express their discontents and they must sometimes feel that doctors and social workers are biased towards taking the patient's point of view. At the same time a strong feeling of duty and humanity makes many relatives accept the burden of caring for a handicapped patient. It is not necessarily good clinical practice to accept this situation as a justification for "community care". ... In accepting it the clinician is tacitly assuming that it is better for the patient to be at home and there may be a built-in tendency, therefore, not to inquire too closely into the social circumstances of the family in case evidence is found to the contrary'.

We would endorse these comments. Now that there is a voluntary association acting in the interests of patients and relatives, what services should they press for? The first would seem to be adequate information and advice.

Information and Advice

In the early stages of the acute illness it may be difficult to make a precise diagnosis and prognosis and the cautious pronouncements of the doctor may be mistaken by relatives for evasion. Once the condition has become established, however, there is every reason why the relative should be given full guidance about the nature of schizophrenia and the factors influencing its course. This form of counselling is very poorly developed at the moment, compared with the situation in other fields such as physical handicap, mental retardation and early childhood autism, where experimental counselling schemes have been set up and evaluated. A good deal of relevant knowledge is available from scientific research into the consequences of social overstimulation and social understimulation and from surveys such as the present one, in which relatives have reported the results of their own trial and error efforts.

The main problems in 'management' are social withdrawal and associated behaviour, odd beliefs or experiences and associated behaviour, social control, secondary reactions to handicap such as depression, attempts at suicide, underconfidence and a lack of willingness to collaborate in sensible methods of rehabilitation (or its converse, a denial of handicap and an unrealistic optimism), the management of medication, the prescription of services, the relatives' own reactions, which can be helpful or unhelpful but must always be carefully considered with some trusted counsellor.

What relatives have told us during this survey suggests that many have discovered for themselves that a non-emotional pressure to attain achievable standards, leaving the patient a good deal of control, is the best way to counteract social withdrawal and slowness. Withdrawal is protective up to a point but beyond that it is damaging. Relatives found that social interaction was exhausting for patients. Possibly this is because of the difficulty of communication in schizophrenia due to a disturbance of the process of thinking, which interferes both with understanding what other people mean when they talk or use non-verbal language and with the patient's ability to express himself. In addition to this, there is often a marked reduction in the patient's ability to communicate using non-verbal language, i.e. through facial expression, posture, gait, gesture and so on. These are intrinsic handicaps which must be recognised before patient and relatives can work out techniques of overcoming or compensating for them. It is not surprising that patients were often exhausted by activities (such as holding down a simple job) which most people would be able to take in their stride.

Similarly, relatives had discovered that it was useless to contradict a patient who expressed delusional ideas. This led only to arguments which might make matters worse. The patient *does* have these experiences even if he interprets them incorrectly. A more realistic aim is to try to limit the effect of such ideas upon the patient's public behaviour. Many patients were well able to understand this and to limit odd behaviour such as talking to themselves, and the expression of odd ideas, to private occasions. Another important clue, noticed by one or two relatives, was that too much intrusion on the patient's privacy (too much 'social stimulation') might lead to a recrudescence of hallucinations or odd ideas. Patients are extremely sensitive to criticism particularly concerning problems that it is not within their power to change. Like the rest of us, they need to be successful occasionally, to be rewarded when they achieve something that, for them, is difficult, even though luckier people might have found it easy.

The idea has to be grasped that many of the problems encountered in schizophrenia, such as a liability to hallucinatory experiences, can be most usefully viewed as arising from a number of underlying impairments which are, in themselves, no more and no less to be feared than blindness or paraplegia. The necessity for learning the most practicable ways of living and for finding new enjoyments in spite of the handicapping effect of these impairments is of much the same order. To become afflicted by schizophrenia or by blindness is a tragedy. Having said that, life has to go on, both for patient and relative. Virtually none of the relatives we talked to had received any sensible advice about the nature of schizophrenia or about what steps could be taken to find ways round the problems that inevitably ensued. The problem of social control has to be considered realistically in the same way. Some part of the patient's behaviour is certainly under his control and a clearly expressed view from doctors and social workers that certain types of behaviour cannot be tolerated at home is very helpful both to patients and relatives.

Another difficulty was that few relatives knew of others with the same kinds of problem. The National Schizophrenia Fellowship can help here if it can publicise its activities widely enough. When relatives feel they are doing something to help the patients and themselves they gain in self-respect and become better able to resist uninformed pressures from other members of their own families or the general public.

Counselling skills of this very specific kind are not taught to medical or nursing specialists, let alone to general medical practitioners or social workers, at the moment. Even supposing, however, that they were, there is the problem that the supporting network of services on which the counsellors would need to call is frequently defective at a number of crucial points.

Medical services

The main complaints about medical services were concerned with the difficulties of obtaining early diagnosis, lack of explanation about the nature of the condition, non-availability of genetic counselling and problems in obtaining adequate help in an emergency. There was less dissatisfaction with the hospitals, though there were comments about old-fashioned buildings, overcrowding and lack of staff. Very few relatives mentioned the 'stigma' attached to going into a mental hospital rather than a psychiatric unit in general hospital. Some relatives felt that patients did not stay in hospital long enough so that the burden of responsibility was not really lessened when admission was arranged. However, there was also little appreciation of the fact that the social functions of mental hospitals have now theoretically been transferred to local authority services. Where the patient was assiduous in attending the general practitioner or psychiatric clinic in order to continue medication, all sorts of other problems seemed to be less. Work on the long-term preventive effects of the phenothiazine drugs has confirmed this. Long-acting phenothiazines, given by injection, are particularly useful when the patient tends to forget to take daily tablets.

Social Services

There was much more criticism of the lack of supportive social services. In particular, day centres and hostels (or group homes) were often not available. Most of the patients in our survey were not gainfully employed. Day centres combine the dual functions of occupying the patient's day ('the long empty hours stretching between breakfast and bedtime') and of reducing the amount of face-to-face contact between patient and relative which often results in a disastrous rise in tension. Relatives were very grateful when patients *were* able to attend day centres or, better still, sheltered workshops. It was clear that ordinary work in competitive employment was beyond most of the patients and that those who could work usually came home completely exhausted. Recent scientific work confirms this impression. The ordinary occupational rehabilitation services are not geared to the problems of schizophrenia and those relatives with experience of Industrial Rehabilitation Units were unimpressed. Probably active rehabilitation units would be better attached to day hospitals, particularly if patients could begin the process of rehabilitation *before* the process of chronicity had become too developed and a mood of non-cooperation had set in. The Department of Employment has issued a number of consultative documents on services for handicapped people and no doubt there will, in time, be improvements. For the moment, however, there remains an urgent need for adequate day centre places in all geographical areas and for an upgrading of one centre in each area to the level of a Remploy factory.

Recent work on hostels and group homes has shown that most local authorities are preoccupied with providing short-term accommodation from which, it is hoped, the patient will eventually be able to be resettled into some more independent domestic setting. Relatives thought this aim was often unrealistic. Hewett and Ryan, in a parallel study to this one, have found that about half of the hostel accommodation used by three south-east London boroughs is provided by voluntary associations. It is of good quality and patients, on the whole, are very content. They want to stay even when they are aware that the length of stay was limited. However, they are expected to work, which limits the intake quite severely. Many of those now accumulating as 'new long-stay' patients in mental hospitals could not be expected to work in competitive employment, but do not need a hospital environment. A combination of day centre and hostel would be ideal. Hostel wardens tend not to expect patients to undertake domestic chores, shopping and cooking as well as their daily occupation, because they are well aware that patients find work itself sufficiently fatiguing. This would be just as true of those unable to work; attendance at a day centre (with its involvement in many kinds of directed activity) can be very exhausting for someone with schizophrenia.

Another advantage of hostels is that they provide heating and lighting free, foster social activity in leisure hours and at weekends, and provide a base from which patients can meet their relatives and friends on an emotionally independent footing. The rent is much lower than unsubsidised digs would be and the amenities much better.

Even in those cases where relatives accepted the presence of the patients at home there was often a feeling that a hostel nearby would be preferable. What one parent called the 'when I am gone' syndrome was also frequently evident. Siblings might not wish to take over a caring role when parents died and parents would feel easier in their minds if a transfer to a suitable hostel could take place in anticipation of any such event.

Few relatives had had experience of 'group homes', which are houses fitted up as bed-sitters and occupied by a number of patients who look after themselves. One or two who had were critical, however, because they thought the patient did not have sufficient skill and drive to look after himself and it sounded as though the group home did not provide nearly such a supportive setting as the hostel, particularly in the evenings and weekends. However, given sufficient social support, group homes and supervised lodgings would extend the range of sheltered residential environments available to patients.

Other practical help which was rarely available but which would have been greatly appreciated included relief arrangements for occasional evenings, weekends and holidays; social clubs which could cope with people with schizophrenic handicaps; financial help, particularly with the patient's unemployment or sickness or supplementary benefit; and 'on call' help with small children when the patient was a mother unable to look after them.

Conclusions

The results of this survey confirm two basic facts: that many people with schizophrenia are severely and chronically handicapped and that their impairments, within limits, are highly reactive to the social environment. The social conditions in which patients live can to some extent determine the severity of disablement. Left to themselves, some relatives do eventually work out, by a method of trial and error, how to react to the patient in such a way that his impairments are minimised and his assets fully exploited. They do not, however, usually obtain much help in understanding this process from professional people, and it is therefore inevitably haphazard and painful and all too often something goes irremediably wrong.

Our first main conclusion is that insufficient recognition is given to the fact that relatives are the real 'primary care' agents. In the case of other chronically disabling conditions, such as paraplegia or blindness or renal failure, techniques of 'management' have beeen worked out in some detail so that patients and relatives can anticipate and prevent many of the likely problems and know what to do when crises occur. Something similar is available, at least experimentally, for the parents of mentally retarded or psychotic children. Experimental schemes need to be set up in which all the knowledge now available about the factors which influence the course of schizophrenia is applied to achieve optimum conditions for a number of families containing a schizophrenic patient. The results could then be systematised and made more widely available to doctors, social worker and nurses. Some of the problems of non-cooperation from patients, which loomed so large in this survey, could have been avoided if such counselling had been available from the beginning. Once attitudes of distrust have been allowed to develop it is much more difficult to obtain cooperation.

Such a counselling scheme, however, would be useless without good supporting services. Facilities for early detection, treatment of acute relapses and provision of long-term medication are already available in most places and the main need is that they should be used in a rational and coordinated way. Even then, however, although the course of schizophrenia would undoubtedly be smoother, there would often still remain a core of 'negative' handicaps (withdrawal, slowness and apathy) which necessitated the provision of a range of protected environments. These will often be needed permanently. Day centres are still not available in some areas and, when they are, do not provide working conditions in which schizophrenic patients receive the optimum supervision which will bring out the best that they can achieve. Moreover, day centres do not provide for evenings or weekends and not all patients can live at home or in lodgings.

Our second main conclusion is that many schizophrenic patients would be able to lead fuller and more independent lives if small hostels were available in the neighbourhood from which they could go out to work or to attend day centres, and where the principles of 'management' were well understood. Living with handicap is exhausting for the patient and it may be too much to expect that many will be able both to do competitive work and to maintain a domestic role as well. These hostels would provide a permanent home but the existence of close ties with relatives living nearby would also provide a focus for social activity. Group homes might fulfil the same purpose if plenty of supervision and support were available. There will still, however, be a small group of patients who need much closer supervision and care such as could only be available in a more closed community.

Our third main conclusion is that the attitudes of patients, relatives, professional people and the general public towards schizophrenia are often uninformed and harmful. There is little doubt that the creation of an integrated network of services along the lines we have discussed, in which each patient would be able to obtain the particular combination of services which he needed at each stage of his life, would in itself contribute to a new understanding of the nature of schizophrenia and a new sympathy for those affected.

Selected References

Apte, R. Z. (1968). *Half-way Houses*. Occas. Papers on Soc. Admin. No. 27 London: Bell.

Barton, R. (1959). *Institutional Neurosis*. Bristol: Wright.

Bennett, D. H. *et al.* (1972). Non residential services for the mentally ill. In: Wing J. K. and Hailey A. M. *op. cit*: chapter 7.

Brown, G. W. *et al.* (1966). *Schizophrenia and Social Care*. London: Oxford University Press.

Brown, G. W., Birley J. L. T. and Wing, J. K. (1972). Influence of family life on the course of schizophrenic disorders: A replication. *Brit. J. Psychiat. 121*, 241–258.

Early, D. F. (1965). Domestic resettlement and economic rehabilitation. In: *Psychiatric Hospital Care*. Ed: Freeman H. London: Balliere, Tindall & Cassell.

Hewett S. and Ryan, P. (1972). A study of residents financially supported by three London boroughs in hostels for the 'adult mentally ill'. Unpublished report. Institute of Psychiatry.

Hirsch, S. *et al.* (1973). Out-patient maintenance of chronic schizophrenic patients with long-acting fluphenazine. *Brit. Med. J. 1*, 633–637.

Kaplan, B. (1974). *The Inner World of Mental Illness: a Series of First-Person Accounts of What It Was Like*. New York: Harper and Row.

Leff, J. and Wing, J. K. (1971). Trial of maintenance therapy in schizophrenia. *Brit. Med. J. 3*, 599.

Mann, S. and Cree, W. (1974). The 'new long-stay' in mental hospitals. Unpublished report. Institute of Psychiatry.

Stevens, B. (1972). Dependence of schizophrenic patients on elderly relatives. *Psychol. Med. 2*, 17–32.

Stevens, B. (1973). Role of fluphenazine decanoate in lessening the burden of chronic schizophrenics on the community. *Psychol. Med. 3*, 141–158.

Wing, J. K. (1974). Impairments in schizophrenia: A rational basis for social treatments. To be published.

Wing, J. K. and Brown, G. W. (1970). *Institutionalism and Schizophrenia*. London: Cambridge University Press.

Wing, J. K., Bennett, D. H. and Denham, J. (1964). *Industrial Rehabilitation of Long-Stay Schizophrenic Patients*. MRC Memo No. 42. London: HMSO.

Wing, J. K. and Hailey, A. M. (1972). *Evaluating a Community Psychiatric Service: The Camberwell Register 1964–71*. London: Oxford University Press.

FOUR Schizophrenia from Within
edited by Professor John Wing

THE MAIN POINT of this collection of essays is to help people understand what schizophrenia is like from the point of view of those who have experienced it 'from within'. It consists simply of seven personal accounts of what it is like to have schizophrenia. Inevitably, the most literate and articulate have to speak for the large majority of their fellow sufferers who find it much more difficult to express themselves. The seven authors do manage, between them, to convey a vivid impression of the experience of schizophrenia, particularly in the acute stages. Something of the fearful suffering often involved is portrayed. So too is the frustration of handicap; of knowing you are constricted by bonds that other people do not have; of feeling how unfair it is that the disability is 'invisible', so that the sympathy extended to the more evidently disabled is withheld.

Those who have tried to deny that schizophrenia 'exists' have much to answer for. They have inflamed ancient prejudices and helped to increase suffering. By contrast, all the essays in this book contain a message of hope. Human beings have to face all sorts of disasters. They survive. These seven people have survived. They are working out for themselves a way of living with their own condition; learning how they can not only find peace but also make their own contribution to society. Above all, they dispose of some of the cruel stereotypes which fearful people have constructed around the idea of madness. These men and women are not strangers from another planet or monsters to be hunted or butts to be derided. They are not recognisable as characters in detective novels. They are ordinary people describing experiences which anyone, with an effort of the imagination, can understand to be frightening, bewildering and potentially destructive of personality. The authors make some suggestions as to how other people can help to prevent the most severe effects occurring but they also emphasise self-help.

Indeed one of the most interesting features of what the authors have to say is that, in some cases, it is possible eventually to achieve a considerable degree of insight, so that the individual is able to recognise the experiences for what they are and apply preventive methods before they get out of control.

The authors did not much enjoy writing about their past problems but they were willing to do so primarily because they hoped it would help understanding in other sufferers, in relatives, in professional people and in sympathetic members of the general public.

Introduction

What is schizophrenia?

People who have not themselves come into contact with schizophrenia are often puzzled to know what the term means. There are many stereotypes to choose from. The most fashionable and mystifying presents schizophrenia as a sort of distorting mirror held up to society, in which, if we read the blurred images aright, we can discover the truth about ourselves and our future. Unfortunately each prophet puts forward a different interpretation of the message, usually in terms of some high-flown and untestable theory. Such fringe movements are ephemeral by their nature and would be of little interest except that they have been taken up and plugged in a big way by the media during the past fifteen years so that they have had a considerable influence on public opinion. On the whole, this influence has been harmful.

In the first place, the search for oracular truth has resulted in a denial of personal disability and suffering. The 'poetry of schizophrenia' sounds very romantic but the truth is that great artists, like Nijinsky and Hölderlin, who have developed the condition, lost their creativity altogether. In the second place, the theorists have all looked for scape-goats. Some have found the cause in capitalist society, others in the subtle infiltration of Communist ideas. Such inanities matter little, but a more destructive approach has been to blame the parents; people who are in no position to defend themselves and who, in these days of 'community care', bear the main burden apart from the sufferers themselves. Finally, there are stereotypes, expressed in old wives' tales, in folk lore and in the ignorant fantasies of thriller writers.

The sad thing is that during these same fifteen years our knowledge of schizophrenia has increased considerably, not least in understanding the way in which environmental factors influence the course of the acute and chronic manifestations.

The essays collected here illustrate some of this progress. But the major point made by all the authors is that the schizophrenic experience is a real one. To discuss schizophrenia as a myth created by psychiatrists is not simply ignorant; it denigrates and denies experiences which, although so rare that only about one per cent of the population experience them, are nevertheless not at all imaginary. These authors know what they are talking about. Moreover, in spite of the restrictions imposed by the condition, each one remains uniquely individual. None is 'a schizophrenic' — a term as insultingly depersonalising as 'a leper' or 'a black'. And most important of all, there is hope and inspiration to be drawn from the fact that, like many others faced with personal and social disadvantages, they have striven with some success to find a way of life that is satisfying and useful in spite of their difficulties.

The acute schizophrenic syndromes

Two-thirds of the people given a diagnosis of schizophrenia in two recent large-scale international studies described experiences belonging to a central syndrome which has been illustrated by most of the authors of these essays. Contrary to a widespread belief, these experiences can be recognised reliably by trained psychiatrists interviewing in languages as diverse in structure as Chinese, Hindi or Yoruba and belonging to widely different cultural backgrounds. The central syndrome consists of experiences such as thought insertion, thought broadcast, thought withdrawal, voices heard discussing the individual in the third person or commenting on his actions or thoughts, and perceptions of the physical or social environment which are distorted in various specific ways. For example, the world may take on an intensely personal reference so that everything that happens seems to be directed specifically at the individual and to contain a special message for him.

Such 'primary' experiences are likely to be interpreted

differently by different people. By an effort of imagination, we can understand how we might react if we ourselves had such experiences. The temptation to develop 'delusional' explanations, in terms of ideas which otherwise would seem to come straight from science fiction, is obviously great. Suppose, for example, that someone hears his own thoughts being echoed or repeated or spoken aloud in his head, so loud that he feels that anyone standing nearby must be able to overhear them. Suppose that the experience goes further; that some of the thoughts have a distorted quality and do not appear to be his own, or that they seem to come from outside, i.e. are heard as 'voices'. We are dealing here with a disorder of the most characteristically human experience, 'internal language'. It is entirely comprehensible that the affected individual will consider all sorts of explanations including hypnotism, telepathy, radio waves, spirit possession and so on, depending on his cultural background. This effort of the imagination can help us to understand what is happening in the early stages of schizophrenia. In addition, we can see why fear, panic and depression are so common, and why judgement is so often distorted.

Experiences like these can occur after taking amphetamine or in chronic alcoholism or as part of the aura in certain kinds of epilepsy. Evelyn Waugh gave a vivid description, in *The Ordeal of Gilbert Pinfold*, of a hallucinatory state due to chronic intoxication by bromide and alcohol. It is when no obvious cause of this kind is present that the term 'schizophrenia' is used.

Other acute syndromes are also given the label of 'schizophrenia'. For example, the paranoid syndromes involve an intense conviction which, so far as other people can see, is demonstrably false. From the point of view of others the person concerned is 'deluded'. Often these ideas take the form of delusions of persecution but they may also be grandiose or religious in nature or purely idiosyncratic. Sometimes there might only be a single over-valued idea, for example that a person's nose is too large even though no-one else can see anything the matter with it. Such a preoccupation can ruin his life, drive him from one plastic surgeon to another, spoil his personal relationships and deprive him of any peace or satisfaction. All these syndromes can occur without any evidence that the central experiences described earlier have ever been present. Another, even more heterogeneous set of conditions is based on more tenuous clues in behaviour, in emotional expression or in ways of thought. Someone who becomes more and more solitary, odd and self-absorbed may be called schizophrenic although he has not described any of the experiences making up the central syndromes and does not seem to be deluded.

This is not the place to consider whether all these syndromes ought to be grouped under the same label. The evidence for and against is extremely complicated and gives rise to much controversy. The central syndromes are commonest, our knowledge about them is greatest, and there is a good deal of agreement about course and treatment. The remainder of this brief review will therefore be devoted to a summary of the present state of knowledge about a large central group of 'schizophrenias'.

Before considering various types of explanation for the acute schizophrenic experiences it is important to consider their relationship to more chronic syndromes.

The chronic schizophrenic syndromes

The acute syndromes we have just been considering are often preceded, accompanied or followed by a condition of social disablement. Nowadays, this is not severe except in about one quarter of cases. Two main groups of characteristics stand out as particularly disabling. The first is a syndrome of 'negative' traits such as emotional apathy, slowness of thought and movement, underactivity, lack of drive, poverty of speech and social withdrawal. These traits tend to occur together. They limit the individual's social performance at virtually any task, creative or routine, personal or social. For example, the most severely impaired person can convey little information through the use of verbal or non-verbal language, the facial expression is wooden, the voice is monotonous, the bodily posture and gait is stiff, little use is made of gesture, words are few and may convey little meaning. Such limitations can be very handicapping indeed.

In addition to this syndrome there may be another, in which the individual does not seem to be able to think to a purpose but goes off on a side-track owing to some unusual association to a chance stimulus and thus gives the impression of vagueness, confusion and incoherence. There may be long-standing delusions and hallucinations and accompanying manifestations in behaviour; e.g. the individual may laugh and talk 'to himself'.

The two kinds of chronic syndrome are not unrelated. Social withdrawal, for example, may be in part a reaction to the individual's experience that his attempts at communicating with other people are received with bafflement and a more or less polite brush-off. Attempts at communication are actually painful. However, this is by no means the whole explanation of social withdrawal or slowness.

Apart from these two types of impairment, the liability to further acute attacks in which the central schizophrenic experiences return must also be regarded as a kind of disability. Following an acute attack there remains a definite vulnerability to further breakdowns of a similar kind. Nevertheless, about half the people who experience a first attack have a good outcome over the following five years. In about a quarter there is a relapsing course and in the remaining quarter a condition of chronic disablement is reached.

This, in brief, is what is meant by 'schizophrenia'. The term will not be used in this chapter in any other way. We can now consider the various theories put forward to explain the nature and origin of the central schizophrenic syndromes.

Schizophrenia as an illness

Putting forward a diagnosis is like putting forward a scientific theory; it can be tested. Is it useful or not? The most obvious test is whether it is helpful to the individual concerned. For example, does it accurately predict a form of treatment which reduces disability without leading to harmful side-effects? Does it give some idea of the future course and outcome? At the very least, can the affected person and the relatives be given the consolation, if there is no known method of cure, that there are other people with the same condition, that it has a name and that there are ways (perhaps best learned from other sufferers) of coping?

A further way in which a diagnosis can be useful is as a means of acquiring new knowledge. This may not be of immediate benefit to sufferers but it may lead to discoveries which will suggest future methods of treatment or prevention.

Before we can use the term 'disease' or 'illness' in any scientific sense, two conditions must be satisfied with a fair degree of reliability. We have already described certain rare experiences which psychiatrists everywhere agree are characteristic of a central schizophrenic syndrome. Historically, the recognition of a syndrome usually comes before the second condition can be satisfied, and schizophrenia is no exception. The second condition is that a firm link must be established between the syndrome and underlying psychobiological abnormalities. These links may be established in several ways. The most immediately useful links are either causal (these may suggest methods of preventing the syndrome from appearing), or therapeutic (these suggest ways of controlling its manifestations). However, other links may also be useful in the long run, by suggesting a more complete theory of the underlying abnormalities, which in turn may eventually indicate more effective methods of prevention or treatment. Links of this more remote kind may be provided by epidemiology, genetics, pathology, biochemistry or neurophysiology.

Taken together, the two kinds of link provide evidence for a disease theory which explains the central schizophrenic syndrome.

Epidemiology is the study of the distribution of disease syndromes in populations and the comparison of their frequency in one subgroup compared with another. There have been many surveys of rural compared with urban populations, developing compared with developed countries, migrant compared with settled groups, people in skilled versus non-skilled occupations, married compared with single, men compared with women, young compared with old. This evidence suggests that schizophrenia occurs in every part of the world where it has been looked for and that nearly all the obvious social concomitants, for example the higher frequency in single people or in those with unskilled occupations, are a consequence rather than a cause of the condition.

Investigations into causes have certainly shown that social factors are important as precipitants but these are non-specific. The individual who develops schizophrenia is more vulnerable than other people to the stresses of everyday life. Toxic precipitants, such as amphetamine and alcohol, and various kinds of brain disease such as temporal lobe epilepsy, can produce the schizophrenic syndromes but again there seems to be little specificity in the action. Most people with temporal lobe epilepsy do not have schizophrenic symptoms.

The genetic evidence is quite strong but again non-specific. It is not just a matter of increasing frequency in blood relatives the closer they approach in relationship to the sufferer. It is not only a matter of higher frequency in identical compared with fraternal twins. It is not even simply a matter of similar frequencies in identical twins whether they are reared together or apart. All these observations are important but the latest series of Danish studies of children of schizophrenic and non-schizophrenic mothers, adopted and non-adopted, make some sort of genetic mechanism or mechanisms very probable indeed. One would have to be very highly motivated to avoid this conclusion. As Seymour Kety says, if schizophrenia is a myth, it is a myth with a strong genetic component. But we are no nearer to understanding the nature of the heredity; here we are back in semi-darkness.

So far, there is no indication of any structural abnormality in the brain and theories about pathology are based on other types of evidence. Thus the distribution in the brain of the nerve fibres which respond to a particular action of the phenothiazine drugs (see below), together with physiological and psychological data, can be used to buttress a speculation that the main area affected is that known as the limbic striatum. The evidence from biochemical and neurophysiological studies is also no more than suggestive although some leads seem very promising.

There are now several forms of medication which will reduce the severity of the schizophrenic experiences and often suppress them altogether. The drugs known as phenothiazines are most widely used. Not only do they help during acute attacks but they act to prevent further relapse if taken regularly. They do not cure schizophrenia any more than insulin (in conjunction with other methods such as diet) cures diabetes, nor do they always suppress all the unpleasant experiences. They are less often successful in ameliorating chronic impairments such as slowness and apathy. However, the effect on the acute syndromes is often dramatic and it is not due to a mere sedation. In fact, sedative drugs are of very little use.

In summary, the cumulative evidence for some sort of disease theory or theories is very striking, though many of the details remain to be worked out. So far, however, it is not possible to link the central schizophrenic syndromes firmly to a specified underlying psychobiological disturbance and until this link is demonstrated we can only claim a very partial understanding of schizophrenia in terms of disease theories. This does not mean there is nothing else to say. Far from it. In the case of many syndromes of severe mental retardation, such as Down's syndrome ('mongolism'), we know a good deal about the underlying somatic abnormality but this does not take us much further than predicting a particular pattern of basic disabilities. Such knowledge is important because it enables us to say what services should be made available, how parents and teachers should be advised to help the child, and what types of environmental action are most likely to be effective in compensating for the disabilities. But the main services required will be educational and social rather than medical. Thus the fact that no cure is available does not end the discussion of how to help: it begins it. We have seen that schizophrenia, too, sometimes becomes a chronic condition. The interaction between individual and environment will therefore determine to a considerable extent what the outcome is likely to be. Quite a lot is known about this interaction.

Social reactivity in schizophrenia

In the formulations of some early psychiatrists it was considered that chronic schizophrenic impairments (or 'deterioration' as it was called) were ruthlessly progressive and that very little could be done to ameliorate the condition. We now know that this view was wrong. In fact, a certain hopelessness about the outcome was one of the reasons why so many people with schizophrenia remained for long years in mental hospitals. Even in the 1930s, when modern ideas where beginning to be introduced, someone admitted for the first time with a diagnosis of schizophrenia stood only a one in three chance of being discharged within two years. After two years the chance of being discharged at all became extremely low. Nowadays only about 5 % stay as long as a year. The significance of the very long stay was that a gradual process of institutionalism set in, during which the individual came to regard his own ability to cope outside hospital as hopeless even when, as happened quite often, the acute schizophrenic syndromes disappeared. There are still long-stay in-patients who do not wish to leave although they would probably be able to do so given help.

During the 1950s and early 1960s, the social methods of helping people which had characterised the period of reform more than a hundred years earlier, were rediscovered and reintroduced. It was shown quite clearly that people with schizophrenia who lived in hospitals providing a good social environment were less handicapped by social withdrawal, slowness and apathy than those in hospitals where reform had not progressed so far. In other words, poverty of the social environment was harmful. This was not only true of hospitals, but of other places of living, including hostels, day centres and the individual's own home.

On the other hand, the vulnerability we discussed earlier was still present. A different kind of response to schizophrenia is social intrusiveness, the opposite of poverty of the social environment. Events which most people take in their stride may prove highly threatening to someone who is liable to develop acute schizophrenic attacks. Even promotion at work or getting engaged to be married, usually regarded as positive and rewarding events, may sometimes be experienced as increasing the pressure too much. Too vigorous attempts at rehabilitation may also lead to relapse. Living at home with relatives who put on too much emotional pressure, or are too critical of the individual's disabilities, can have the same effect.

The difficulties experienced by relatives in trying to come to terms with these problems are described in the previous chapter, 'Schizophrenia at Home', and in the NFS publication, 'Living with Schizophrenia'. The essence of the matter is that the individual handicapped by schizophrenia has to avoid two different kinds of danger. On the one hand, too little social stimulation encourages social withdrawal, slowness and apathy. On the other hand, too much social intrusion can lead to serious difficulties of communication and a recrudescence of the acute schizophrenic experiences. It is like walking a tight-rope.

Handling medication presents further difficulties. There is no doubt that the phenothiazines help not only to suppress the acute experiences but to prevent relapse. On the other hand, they sometimes have undesirable effects and clearly no-one wants to take medication when it is unnecessary. As a general rule (there are exceptions), the more sheltered and unpressured the environment the less medication is necessary. But the protective effect of medication will not overcome a really stressful environment and *too much* withdrawal may also have to be corrected by administration of drugs.

Encouragement to take an interest in social, domestic and vocational activities is often effective if it comes from familiar and trusted individuals and is not accompanied by too much emotional involvement. It is also important that the handicapped person retains control of the extent to which he participates, so that he does not expose himself to a level of stimulation that he experiences as painful, or at least only in carefully graduated doses. There is also the problem of communication. The appearance of the severely handicapped individual with schizophrenia may lead the observer (whether doctor, nurse, social worker or relative) to suppose that attempts at communication are likely to be fruitless, and fewer and fewer attempts are made to reach him. This process can be self-perpetuating because of the temptation that social withdrawal holds out to the sufferer – it is so much easier to give up trying. And the risk of overdoing the attempt at communication is definitely present.

Clearly it is pointless to try to allocate blame when the end result is unsatisfactory. Professional people, relatives and the sufferers themselves have to feel their way by trial and error, using a few principles for basic guidance. The most successful result is likely to come when professional counsel is informed and readily available, when a choice can be made from a range of comprehensive services, including day and residential settings providing shelter graded all the way from full protection (needed only briefly) to subsidised but otherwise open housing, and when the handicapped person and his relatives fully understand the problems of interaction between schizophrenia and the environment.

In the present state of British services, caught half-way in the transfer of responsibility between a running-down mental hospital system and an incomplete community care alternative, it is unfortunately inevitable that conditions will often be far from ideal.

Meanwhile the following essays speak for themselves. They show people coming to terms with frightening and disabling experiences which most of us do not have and cannot understand without an effort of imagination. That the effort is worthwhile the authors make clear.

Thirty-one not out

In this account I will attempt to convey to the reader the experiences of *one* man who has had schizophrenia. It may not be a finished story because schizophrenia is often a recurrent illness. However I am optimistic, as we all must be, when looking to the future. New methods of treatment, more tolerant attitudes among the public in general and more research give a better chance in life to those suffering from this bizarre illness.

At the same time I hope that this account will be useful to sufferers and their relatives, as well as to those concerned with schizophrenia in their professional work. But a word of warning: it is not designed to be a blueprint. On the contrary there are many different facets of the illness and many different symptoms, some of which I have never experienced. Each individual must be treated as unique. I feel that there is no *one* cause of schizophrenia and that research must be directed along these lines. I will attempt to be as impersonal as possible and hope that my criticisms will be constructive in nature.

Background

I was born in 1943 in the middle of a war which was ravaging the world. My father was a farmer and my mother a school-teacher. During the war and while my father was at the front, I was evacuated to the North, as the bombs were exploding all round us. By all accounts I was a normal, healthy baby, although by the age of one I had put on a considerable amount of weight, due to the fact that my grandmother thought I was hungry whenever I cried. After 1945 my father went back to his farm. Mine was a happy childhood with plenty of affection and stimulation. There were plenty of animals on and around the farm to captivate my attention, including over eight cats, two thousand chickens, pigs and cows.

My sister was born in 1947 and we got on well together, although there was the usual aggravation not uncommon in most families. Punishments at home were severe enough to be a deterrent. For a minor offence, being sent to the bedroom for half an hour was the remedy. Sometimes I was a bit rough and this merited a slipper on the backside.

Early school days

My first school was a play-school.

At the age of five I went to kindergarten, travelling on the bus by myself to the school which was five miles away. I found school enjoyable and by reports was above average, especially in subjects like spelling, and reading. So by the age of seven I had a good grounding in the three 'Rs'.

Boarding school

I was first sent away to school in 1950, at the age of seven – an experience which was an unhappy one. I can vividly remember the first day – the tears and the rabbit given to me for consolation.

While in bed with measles one term, I threw a slipper across the dormitory and cracked a lampshade. If this was discovered, I knew the consequences, and lived in a state of fear. However salvation came from an unexpected source. The local priest used to visit the school to hear confessions, and one day I must have expressed my fears or given the priest some idea of how I was feeling. He contacted my father who immediately took me away from the school and threatened to sue the Headmaster.

When telling doctors about this they have tended to dismiss it as unimportant. However, in my opinion, it is the sort of incident, the effects of which should be taken into account when treating somebody who suffers from a mental illness like schizophrenia. On a sensitive child, an experience as traumatic as this could have a profound effect on the personality; paranoia might be the result, although I prefer to be hypothetical in my case, as it is impossible to gauge the effects of such an experience.

By the end of my school career in 1961, I had six 'O' levels, three 'A' levels to my name. In addition I was a school prefect, played cricket for the 1st XI and rugby for the 2nd XV.

University

Having failed to get into Oxbridge, I studied for an honours history degree at a provincial university from 1962 to 1966. It was a big break for me, the urban environment clashed sharply with what I was used to.

I had one or two contacts, but had no difficulty in finding new friends. In my first year I worked hard and played cricket for the university. I passed all my exams, although not without a struggle and was elected Secretary of the Cricket Club.

The first indication of mental illness occurred in 1963 when I was 20. I can remember going to a party and getting very drunk. The next morning I woke up and began to start worrying. What had I done last night? How degrading. Had the alcohol affected my brain? Perhaps one would term these feelings neurotic. But my behaviour was certainly altered. I became very introverted and found it impossible to communicate with my friends. I suffered from loss of concentration – I could not take notes at lectures – I read one page of a book two of three times before moving onto the next page. I couldn't write essays and was compelled to copy them out of books. My memory was hopeless.

My friends realised that something was wrong and tried to help me by taking me out to parties etc – *their* cure for my 'depression'. But this only made matters worse. I wanted to withdraw rather than mix. I wanted to resign from being secretary of the cricket club but was persuaded to continue in office.

In the end I went to see a G.P. who tended rather to dismiss me, telling me to come back if things didn't improve. I did return, and was referred to the Psychiatric Unit at the University. Here I was interviewed and given amitriptyline. When I went home for the vacation, my parents were rather shocked when I told them I was on drugs. They became worried and upset, as this was a new experience for them. However they assured me that things would get better when the cricket season started.

They were right. I recovered speedily and became involved in running the club. It was hard work but therapeutic. I moved to new digs, stopped taking amitriptyline and life was fun again.

My career at university continued, as far as I can remember, without any major upset. I made friends easily and in my final year met a girl who became my first serious friend of the opposite sex. Doubtless Mr. Freud would have something to comment on here!

By 1966 I had become much more of an extrovert and had grown in self-confidence. I could now meet and talk to people from all walks of life. I had been on two camping expeditions in Europe – visiting many countries. I had developed a passionate interest in horse racing, although I was not a heavy gambler. Sport of all kinds was my main hobby and interest.

London

Whilst in my final year at university, I had decided, rather than teaching as a career, to go into the family business.

I therefore started work in the City in the autumn of 1966. It was understood that I should start at the bottom and work my way up.

The work, however, was not stimulating or rewarding, and I had to put up with a fair amount of banter from other employees who considered that I had an unfair advantage.

By 1968 I had become depressed, and the same symptoms had returned – a reversion to the old introversion – a suspicion of other people – and an inability to concentrate. The standard of my work suffered, and I found myself staying behind late to finish. Even outside work my concentration was hopeless. I can well remember playing whist with the family. I was always forgetting what suit was trumps, and sometimes failed to follow suit. Of course I realised that all was not right, but the more one worried about this, the worse it became. My mind was not with the job in hand; and in these circumstances people cannot be expected to perform even the simplest of tasks efficiently.

One day I went to see the Personnel Manager at work and he told me very gently that in his opinion I was not suited to the City; but that, until I found another job, he would keep me on. One of my friends found me a clerical job with a West End building firm, and I moved into a flat just around the corner from the office.

All went well for a time: the change in environment, new

people and a not too strenuous job can be explanations of this. However, the man I was working with fell down some stairs, broke his arm, and was off work for a long time. I met another employee who started to sow the first seeds of doubt in my mind. He was very suspicious of the man with the broken arm, and told me he was a fraud. I had to work hard at this time to make up for my colleague's absence, and I was given £30 bonus for my efforts. However as it was paid out of petty cash, word soon got around; and the acid, biting comments were soon forthcoming.

I was going downhill again – deeper than ever before. I began to start thinking that people were watching me and following me. My work was unbearable because, whereas before I could add up a long column of figures without error, now I could never get the sums right. This was because of the feeling that they were against me.

My parents decided that it would be a good idea for me to visit a specialist in Harley Street.

The doctor asked me whether I wanted to go into hospital. I recall my answer well: 'Half of me does, half of me doesn't'. He immediately picked up the telephone.

It was at least a month before I went into a London teaching hospital: perhaps the worst month of my life. I tried to stay at work, but in the end found it impossible. My friends did their best for me, one of them, Peter, used to visit me almost every night, to take me out to pubs or parties and generally tried to get me out of myself. He probably didn't realise, and I didn't tell him, how my mind was working: that the paranoia had really become established.

Tears were frequent, and there were other delusions apart from the one of being watched and followed. The papers were wrong, and were being printed for my benefit. The wireless was not broadcasting the programmes it should, but special ones for me. The television was the same.

On the night before I went into hospital I didn't sleep at all, and the paranoia reached its climax. I felt an electric current coming down the outside wall and into my bed: someone was trying to kill me before I reached the haven of the hospital. It was 5.00 a.m. and I was so frightened that I rushed through and woke two of the other people in the flat. They chatted to me until it was time for them to go to work.

Hospital in London

I arrived in hospital and was shown into a ward which was occupied by people suffering from various serious ailments – from leukaemia to chest diseases. My delusions of being watched did not abate: I thought that these patients were not ill but were just observing me. Every move and action had their meaning. Fortunately my personality did not disintegrate completely so that I managed to control my behaviour so as not to interfere with the running of the ward. However, I did not tell other people (including my doctors and parents) about all my delusions.

I couldn't read any books or papers because of ideas of reference. I thought that they were going to change my sex! I thought that I had lung cancer and gave up smoking completely, so strong was the delusion. My visitors took on various characteristics: one of my relatives, in my eyes, was dressed like a nun and this started off a chain reaction in my thoughts. All the delusions, on looking back, were totally unfounded. However, at the time they were very real and very alarming.

For the first two nights in the ward I didn't sleep, but eventually, having been given a massive dosage of pills, I went off. It was a long time before I returned to a reasonable state of mind, perhaps four to five weeks. Chlorpromazine was one of the drugs used and doubtless the drugs helped to get me back to normality. But I would also like to mention two other factors which aided my recovery: one was the frequent visits paid by my relatives, and the other was the very high standard of nursing. Pretty and cheerful nurses can make all the difference to a patient suffering from both mental and physical illness, and to those nurses I shall be eternally grateful.

'Rehabilitation'

I had been in hospital for eight weeks and left, restored to sanity, but with no job to go to. I did not know what to do with my life, and was given little advice by the hospital except that a career in agriculture or forestry might be suitable.

Eventually my father got me a job as an agricultural labourer with a farmer we knew.

But the job did not go smoothly. I was taking trifluoperazine at the time and perhaps it was the side effects of the drug that affected my work or perhaps the long lay-off had reduced my capacity. Anyway I started full-time, became part-time on my employer's suggestion and eventually he recommended that I give it up completely. Some mornings I did not feel like going to work and some days I went, but found it hard. My inclinations were to sit on a bale of straw and think the day away. I had started smoking again.

Later in 1969 I took a job as an articled clerk but only stayed for a few months as I found the work boring and difficult.

I went for a holiday to the West Indies in 1970 which proved a great success, and when I returned, prepared to take up a vacancy at a teacher-training college.

Return to study

I was back to my normal energetic self. I was elected to the Students Representative Council, started up a cricket club at the college and was generally a leader among my friends.

I graduated from college and took up a teaching post at a prep school. I was still taking perphenazine and, while at the school, became depressed but not hallucinated. I was disappointed that I could not teach some of the children. After a talk with the Headmaster, who was very sympathetic, I was released from my contract and returned home – again unemployed.

A psychiatric hospital

In the Spring of 1972 I became seriously ill again. The cause this time was unknown to me: perhaps the pressure to get work was a contributory cause. I was selling double-glazing for a short time, and while on this venture, I became deluded once again. Many of the old ideas returned including the usual ones of being watched and followed. I also thought that people were putting drugs in my food and drink. Perhaps I ought to mention the fact that I had been breathalysed in the Summer of 1971 and banned from driving for one year in November 1971.

One day I could stand the pressures no longer. I remember the day well. I was staying with friends and I went across the road to a firm, barged into the office and asked them to order me a taxi to drive me to the doctor: quite illogical you will agree, as I had no connection with the firm, except that I knew someone who worked there. In some ways it was logical, as I thought that people had been watching me on a television screen in the office and that they would thus know what I was doing.

When my G.P. saw me, he went out of the room to make a phone call. While he was away, I left the surgery and got back in the taxi, and asked the driver to drive to the house of a psychiatrist I had once been under. He must have had a surprise but also must have realised that I was not well, as he drove me himself to the hospital.

When I first went in I was of course very ill, one example was the occasion I remember asking one of my doctors if she would make love to me! Another delusion which returned was the one that I was not in that particular hospital. To prove this to myself, I got up one bright Summer morning about 5.00 a.m., put on my slippers and dressing-gown and proceeded to walk to the nearest town. I must have walked about two miles before one of the hospital vans picked me up. I was returned and put under section, which meant that I was no longer a voluntary patient for a certain period of time.

Electroconvulsive treatment

My doctor reacted to this strange behaviour by prescribing a course of ECT. I have no doubt that ECT has beneficial effects on many patients; but to me and many other fellow patients it was a terrifying experience, which I hope I shall never go through again.

Drugs, however, were the main agents used, including haloperidol and flupenthixol among many others.

I used to go home most weekends, which I enjoyed, but I could feel myself becoming attached to the hospital. It was a haven of peace and security in a world of strife and hostility. I had to make the break sooner or later. By the end of September 1972 I was well enough to be discharged with instructions for my injection of flupenthixol every three weeks.

Fit but feeble

Yes I was fit again but had no job. The only post-hospital care I received was a visit to out-patients every so often. There was no social worker, nobody to advise me about the best way of getting work or perhaps the powers that be believed that this task was better left to me. In fact I didn't manage to get work until March 1973, when I became a Clerical Officer with the Civil Service.

Again it was a job below my qualification, but this did not worry me as to be working was more important.

It went quite well for a fairly long period, but I received a critical report about my work being too slow. I explained to my boss that this was an effect of the flupenthixol I was taking; and they should have known this anyway, as I had to go for an interview with the Civil Service psychiatrist before being accepted.

Later on, my reports became more favourable; but tensions started to creep insidiously back, and I was forced to take a break from work. Sickness certificates were provided by my doctor, but the personnel department took a thoroughly dim view of this absence and gave me the option of resignation or dismissal on health grounds.

1974: The turning point?

Last year I kept a diary although the entries are somewhat sketchy during the early part because I was unwell. Here are a few extracts which might be of interest.

Jan. 4th 'A little confused about spaces. Forget about things easily. But not too worried because I've been like this before'.

Jan. 28th 'Meeting. Didn't go, saw J. Played scrabble. Still confused but optimistic. Rang G. She was helpful. Thinking hard: never get tired. Every gesture means something'.

Jan. 30th 'One side of brain working better than the other. Afraid of cancer but feel that everything will be OK'.

Feb. 19th 'Woke up early. Not too bad. Get confused and then annoyed. Somebody trying to sort me out. Glad for help. Have got to help others in order to help self. Good policy for the future. Going to see D. – mustn't forget anything'.

Feb. 27th 'Must decide where to take her or will it be arranged? No I have to arrange it. Important to get out and enjoy myself. Just these feelings.'

Apr. 23rd Still the concentration not right. Reading difficult'.

Perhaps these extracts will give the reader some idea of how my mind was working. What they don't reveal is that I believed that by some marvellous miracle of modern science, and with the help of the double glazing in the house, pictures were being transferred to the house up the road. Up there people were analysing my every thought and action. I know *why* I thought this. It started when my doctor came to see me one day, and made a complimentary remark about the double glazing. Through no fault of his making, a chain reaction of crazy ideas was set up and this affected my behaviour completely. The telephone was being tapped. Of this I was convinced which explains my repeated requests to my father to get the GPO engineer to look at it!

I went up to Harley Street to see a renowned psychiatrist there for a second opinion – instigated by my parents. While we were having a cup of tea in a large London restaurant, I really believed that Eamonn Andrews was going to walk in and say: 'This is Your Life'! I thought I was being filmed from aeroplanes, etc., and that one day I was going to be a famous film star. Whether the film was going to be a tragedy or a comedy, I wasn't quite sure!

Dr. C. – the Harley Street specialist – suggested that I was manic-depressive rather than schizophrenic. I said in response to one question that I never became excited and this probably misled him. He recommended out-patient ECT. Needless to say I refused. But he prescribed lithium carbonate and dothiepin as well as the flupenthixol. The last of these was having some disturbing effects, mainly drowsiness and lethargy. Most of the major tranquillisers have had this effect on me. It is a feeling that somehow I am not functioning to my fullest capacity which is very disagreeable, especially when I have no schizophrenic symptoms. Slight hand tremor, particularly when I am under pressure, is another effect I have noticed. After mentioning this to my doctor he agreed to withdrawal in July, by which time the delusions had retreated. Soon after I stopped taking lithium and dothiepin and since that day have taken no drugs.

I have been very well and am now working as a nurse: a job which I really enjoy, which is not too stressful, which is rewarding and for which I believe I have the necessary qualities. The authorities know all about me which is a good thing, and I am very grateful to them for employing me. I only hope, trust and pray that schizophrenic symptoms will not return; but one must always be on one's guard.

Aspects which I found unhelpful

Split between hospital and the 'world outside'
Many patients leaving hospital find it difficult to adjust to normal life. Some have no job to go to. I feel this factor to be very important because the stress thus created sometimes results in a relapse and eventually a return to hospital.

It is not the doctor's responsibility to rectify this situation; but there should be a link between the hospital and the Department of Employment and the DHSS. The importance of the social worker in this sphere must be emphasised. It is not an easy job to place people with schizophrenia in suitable employment; but the DRO's must do what they can, although we are told that it is not always advisable to sign on as disabled.

The importance of work or activity of some purposeful kind must be stressed, apart from the fact that unemployment destroys pride in oneself.

Lack of stimulation in hospital
I feel that much more could be done for schizophrenic patients in hospital, especially by the nursing staff. Some nurses sit around all day chatting among themselves and reading the newspapers. They are supposed to be nurses and not custodians. They should help to occupy the patients – for example, by playing games with them. The patients must be stimulated as much as possible. Pride in their abilities might well return. Inter-ward competitions could be introduced. In one of the hospitals I was in, the patients used to organise social activities; excellent, but if this is not possible the nurses must take the initiative. I hope that I never hear another nurse say that the object of occupational therapy is 'to get the patients off the ward'.

Employment and Social Security
I have said a little about the Department of Employment; but I would like to reiterate that I found them totally unhelpful in

finding me suitable work. There is a Professional and Executive Register, but apart from giving me an IQ test, telling me that I was lucky to go to university and suggesting that I found out something about personnel management little else was forthcoming.

Social Security was not much better. My experience of waiting over two hours to see an official, of being asked about every detail of my private life, of being visited, of my bank statement being examined have soured me against this Department. When one of the top officials found out that I had been in a mental hospital, his comment was acid: 'That explains your behaviour'.

The schizophrenic patient is probably regarded as unemployable by many in the Department of Employment. This attitude must be changed if the sufferers from this illness are going to receive constructive help.

Aspects which I have found to be helpful

Good medical care
Perhaps I have been fortunate in receiving the best treatment I could have hoped for. For a start I know my G.P. well. He takes a great interest in my welfare and is always helpful. This is important – a feeling of mutual trust – an inclination on the part of the patient to tell all. Only by this method can the right treatment be prescribed.

The same is true of my psychiatrist. He is easy to talk to and willing to listen, and he will agree with some of my opinions as to the treatment necessary.

Self Help
One set of figures published fairly recently says that 25 % of schizophrenics make a total recovery. This percentage may well have increased. Another 50 % make reasonably good progress.

A psychiatrist will be able to help you. Drugs will help you. But these will not cure on their own. Self-help, I feel to be very important. The methods are different for each individual, and for some it is obviously easier than others. It is not always possible to help oneself when one is ill; but when better one ought to be able to put up some sort of barrier against a relapse. I am very much in favour of schizophrenic patients trying to understand their handicap by reading about the illness and talking to others who suffer. It is a matter of learning from experience. In my case, I have realised that certain situations tend to bring on symptoms. Of course, there is a sensitivity in myself and I have to try to harden my emotions and cut myself off from potentially dangerous situations. For example, I now tend to avoid contact with people who antagonise me or whom I seem to upset. I sometimes find myself getting worked up about some topic — it might be something political or religious, for example, or it might be the general stupidity of certain people's attitudes or behaviour — and I then tell myself to cool down; to accept rather than attack. I am sure this is the right way for me to cope.

At times like these, when I get worked up, I often experience a slight recurrence of delusional thoughts. I begin to notice coincidences which otherwise I should not have noticed. I might meet someone I hadn't expected to see. Then I might start testing some delusional theory. Let me see whether that car turns the corner behind me. If so, is it still there several turnings later? Then it must be following me! I now feel that I have sufficient knowledge of myself to know that this kind of thinking is dangerous. I can control my mind sufficiently to prevent such thoughts getting out of control and destroying my inner self.

Since I have joined the National Schizophrenia Fellowship my attitude has improved and so has my health. I wish I could say that I had found some books that were useful, but in fact the most helpful one was not meant for a popular readership at all. This was the book on schizophrenia by the late Professor Frank Fish. The books by R. D. Laing, such as *The Divided Self* and *Society, Madness and the Family*, I found interesting but they could have done much harm by turning me against my parents and family. I am glad that has not happened.

Avoid over-stressful situations but don't go too far
This is important to me because stress is one of the major factors which can lead to a recurrence of schizophrenia. We are advised to take up a not too stressful occupation; yes, very important.

Perhaps emotional stress is even more important. I try to avoid people who antagonise me or vice-versa. I have plenty of friends and many of them know about me and help me in various ways. However, not all of them want to hear about my experiences, so that in one's social life perhaps it is advisable to keep quiet about these, especially where sympathy is lacking. A sense of humour certainly helps me where stress is concerned, and if it can be developed, so much the better. These are some ways in which the sensitivity, which many people with mental illness possess, can be counteracted; but to suggest that one is better than another or that these are the only methods would be misguided.

Avoidance can go too far. In my behaviour this was manifest, for example, by not getting up before 10 o'clock, going to bed early, not going to parties or pubs, and not mixing with my friends. I developed a total negativism towards other people. The reason in my case was that I felt inadequate. The lack of concentration, the delusions, the suspicions in my mind, made it impossible for me to converse. I would stand in a group of people and not take part at all. I *wanted* to contribute but could not do so. Consequently, when I went out to meet people I came back feeling almost desperate. I found that alcohol helped social contact and sometimes I drank far too much. I now realise the danger of that though I am not a teetotaller. I always wanted to feel that there was some social support even when I was most withdrawn and could not, for the time, bear any company. Much social withdrawal, in my experience, is a reaction to one's own inadequacies. Sometimes the feeling is so great that one *must* be alone. Withdrawal is then protective but it cannot last forever. Little by little you have to expose yourself to society and learn how to cope.

Work is a very important part of this process. Everyone needs to keep mentally occupied and this is especially true of people with schizophrenia. Work is a great therapy. If my periods of convalescence are too long I tend to get lazy and become unmotivated. What I found tiring, at times, was the effort involved in making myself do things. For example, to get out of a chair and go for a walk required a great deal of effort. I seemed to be apathetic, perhaps because of the feeling of having to start yet again to build my life fearing that, even when I have rebuilt it, it may again collapse. Perhaps a good parallel is a child trying to build a house with bricks who gives up because it keeps on falling down. I believe that quite a few people with schizophrenia drop out completely because the apathy takes a complete hold.

I myself am now training for a certificate as a state enrolled nurse in a hospital dealing with the mentally retarded. Caring for these handicapped people has helped me considerably. I would like to take a higher qualification in nursing at a later date. Perhaps I could add that I should like to see a better paid nursing profession, particularly in the mental health field. This would attract more entrants and allow a better selection. Human qualities such as kindness, concern, patience and tolerance are not handed out to nurses during a training course; they have to be there from the beginning.

Now that I am motivated I no longer feel that a great effort is required, in fact I have to make sure that I don't become hyperactive.

In summary, avoidance of situations which the person with schizophrenia has learned are stressful is very important. Relaxation at times when symptoms are beginning, and understanding of one's sensitivity, will help to stop the reaction going out of control. Rational avoidance can reduce stress. But this reaction must not be allowed to go so far that apathy takes over completely.

Family and friends

My relatives have been very helpful and I appreciate the fact that I come from a close family who are very concerned about my welfare. It is important, however, for parents not to become over-protective once the patient is back to normal. If he or she wants to live away from home, this can often be beneficial as it avoids the emotional stresses that exist in the home. But it is important that the schizophrenic patient always has somewhere 'safe' to go if ill: he must never feel lost, abandoned or without hope.

Relatives and friends, too, need to try to understand what schizophrenia is like. They will then realise how helpful they can be, even just by offering a shoulder to lean on, or a sympathetic audience to what seem to be crazy ideas. It is so difficult to understand that these ideas emerge from real experiences. They are not just made up for effect! But this understanding must also mean that, sometimes, they have to accept that the person with schizophrenia will be unable to take contradiction, particularly if it is expressed in a hostile way. Encouragement and advice can be very helpful if they are offered but not if they are forced. The expression of an alternative point of view, about how it affects relatives and friends, is acceptable if it is phrased in a sympathetic way. But the most helpful response of other people is concern. I always knew that at least some of my friends cared. And laughter, I found a great tonic.

Drugs

Some I have found very helpful: some not so. Every drug has side effects: in some cases these can be controlled. One drug will suit one person: one another. The phenothiazines are widely used for the treatment of schizophrenia: and they have produced remarkable results because they control symptoms like delusions and hallucinations. When I am well I personally dislike flupenthixol because it makes me inefficient. I will never forget the occasion when I had to drive from Yorkshire to London whilst suffering from the effects of this drug. I was asleep the whole way down and it was very dangerous. I also disliked it because I felt incapacitated, and after giving these opinions to my psychiatrist he agreed to my request of withdrawal from the drug. On the other hand it may have better results with other people.

Medication is obviously very important and should be an integral part of the treatment; but therapy of another kind should also be used. The drugs will tranquillise or stimulate; but will they cure the basic problems of phobias which exist in the mind? My method of achieving the latter is 'self-therapy'. If one can learn to control the delusions which can take over one is more than half-way along the road to recovery.

Attitudes

Perhaps the virtues most needed in looking after people with schizophrenia are understanding, tolerance, love and patience. I know that parents, relatives, nurses, doctors, etc., must often lose all hope. But it is always worth remembering that the sufferer is often undergoing a similar experience. The ability to listen is important. On one occasion I couldn't sleep at night and so turned on the radio. The radio told me that I was being trained as a double-agent. I was naturally scared and so went through and chatted to my parents. They didn't dismiss my feelings out of hand, but listened and tried to reason with me. Although I was still convinced that I was right and they were wrong, I felt better. I feel that it is better not to dismiss a delusion and to tell the doctor about it. He may be able to give advice on the best way of dealing with a certain situation.

As for direct help different sufferers demand different types of help. Sometimes parents tend to impose on their children, even when they are over twenty-five years old. This is a mistake because the sufferer is never going to be self-reliant. My parents have always tried to keep me active as possible, even when I just wanted to sit in a chair all day. They always encouraged me in my quest for work. They reminded me about taking medication. But self-pity and self-absorption have always been discouraged. There was inevitably tension, but there always will be because by its very nature schizophrenia is a 'splitting' illness. We just have to make the best out of situations which are sometimes desperate, and to look forward to the future, because I have found that the future does contain hope.

Fortunately my marriage has been a happy one

I started work at a bank at the age of 16, after having had a good education and obtaining my school certificate in five subjects.

I soon found the work interesting but very worrying. It was all the balancing, everything had to agree right down to the very exact penny. A certain amount of work had to be done and balanced each day. We were not allowed to go home until it did. Some days there was no trouble and we went home early but *usually* we could not balance so we had to stay and work overtime. Twice a year at the end of June and December was the Balance, when a lot of overtime was worked. As a result of all this overtime and worry my health started to decline. I was 22.

My parents tell me that they noticed I was not my usual self about one year before I had my breakdown. I had had the flu in the January and gone back to work after having a fortnight off. It was soon afterwards that very occasionally I came out with some rather peculiar sayings. My mother tells me that I started complaining to her that people were talking about me behind my back. My mother did say to me on several occasions that she thought I was imagining it and that if they were talking about me they might be complimentary things but I always insisted they were all against me and were saying detrimental things about me. Then one day (it was Saturday, 1st February, and we were very busy that day), I did not leave the bank till about two o'clock when I came home for lunch. I sat down at home and my mother says I just started talking a load of utter rubbish. My poor mum said that I was not going back to the bank until I was well and I believe she called the doctor in. It was then that he arranged for me to see the specialist at the general hospital and he sent me to a psychiatric hospital.

I was first examined very thoroughly but the doctors could not find anything wrong physically and put it all down to 'nerves', and I started a course of electrical shock treatment. All I remember was that I was given an injection first thing in the morning and then about ten o'clock time we lay on the beds and had this shock treatment which consisted of another injection this time in the arm by the elbow given by a doctor. I then went immediately to sleep and do not remember anymore until I woke up about twelve o'clock time ready for dinner.

All during February and March I felt very ill, and depressed. The *depression* was the worst part of the illness. I complained of hearing voices telling me to do different things, which I felt compelled to do. I was given drugs three times a day. I think they were big chlorpromazine tablets. It was during this time that I felt everyone was against me even the nurses and doctors.

The birds which nested in the trees outside the ward always upset me in the morning waking me up early with their noise. I complained they were talking about me, detrimentally. I cannot remember what I thought they said about me though.

About the middle of March I stopped taking the tablets and used to put them down the toilet. I suddenly noticed one morning on being given the tablets that the sister got them out of a box which was kept locked up and marked POISON. This did it. I then felt they were all poisoning me. At the end of March I was getting worse and everybody began to wonder why. So I was closely watched. They then realised that I did not swallow my tablets so they made me, by not letting me leave the room until I had swallowed them all. Soon I began to pick up and get better. I did feel a bit better by Easter which was in April that year.

When I went into hospital my mum and dad were very good

and always came and visited me whenever they could. They say that I did not clean my teeth, wash myself or comb my hair for the first two months in there. I just existed till I felt better in April when I gradually started to look after myself again. I used to sit all by myself and would hardly say anything to anyone in hospital. A lady who was a retired teacher was put in charge of me. She was a great help especially with seeing that I only had the allowed breakfast on the days I was having treatment. When I was first in hospital I know that I could not sit down for long and I used to walk up and down the corridors trying desperately to get out.

I started coming home for weekends at the beginning of May. By June I was discharged from hospital and my parents were very good and took me to Devon for a holiday before I started back at the bank. I was still on pills though but they took me off chlorpromazine and put me on some others. They were trifluoperazine (blue tablets) and some white tablets which I cannot remember the name of now.

I stayed at the bank until September a little over a year later, then I decided as I felt ill again I would have to get another job. Banking was definitely making me ill again. So I got another job at a firm across the road from the bank, doing much the same kind of work on an accounting machine but there was no pressure there. You just did what you could in the time you worked there. There was no overtime at all. I worked from 9.00 a.m. to 5.30 p.m. and then I was finished each day. I stayed with them until one day in June when I came home early in tears. I just felt terribly depressed and could not stop crying. I got the sack through coming home early and I went to the doctor who sent me to see the specialist at the general hospital again. He put me on some very strong pills but I gradually became much worse. I saw the specialist in September and we decided between us that I should go into hospital again for observation. While in hospital I became gradually worse and had another course of shock treatment which finished just about Christmas. I then improved very slowly at first and I was discharged from hospital in July. I stayed at home then for quite a few years under my own family doctor and saw the specialist at the general hospital every three months.

About two years ago I met my husband and after about four

months courtship we decided to get married. My own doctor told me that it would be a big risk as it would either 'make or break' me. These were his own words to me. Fortunately our marriage has been a happy one and I have now gone off taking the drugs I have been on for over eighteen years under the specialist who I see now about every six months. I feel a lot better now without tablets as they made me very tired and sleepy. The only thing that worries me now is being in and out of jobs all the time. I started this job three weeks ago but I have got the sack again so will have to look for another job again. The employer's reason for sacking me is that I am *too slow*.

Well I am only too thankful that it only lasted four months the first time and that now I am well recovered. I hope that this account will be of help to other sufferers, and to those who are trying to help.

Schizophrenia from within

Family and early years

I had loving parents with middle-class backgrounds. My family was always very comfortably off, and there is no trace of madness on either side, going back for several generations. I had no brothers, but two sisters – both perfectly normal. I can think of no relevant traumatic experience from childhood. I was a late reader, but after that I was always very successful academically at boarding school. I was nearly always moderately happy with a wide range of interests.

When I was in my 'teens, these interests included telepathy. I became interested in the subject not only because of the many books I had read which mentioned it, but because it seemed to fit in with the occasional para-normal experience. I would now and then have the feeling I had seen or heard something that was not really there, the occasional strange thought suddenly coming into my head as if from nowhere. My interest in the subject at that time was in no way obsessional. It was just one interest among very many.

At Christmas 1949, when I was twenty-one, and home on vacation from university, all was going well. I was enjoying the social life at college and I was not over-working. By that time, I believed I could sense people's moods and sometimes eavesdrop on their thoughts. I also believed I could, to some extent, use telepathic force to change their moods. I was intent on developing this power – I had recently bought a book on teaching oneself yoga and was using it in my experiments.

First breakdown

I eventually felt I could go into a crowded restaurant and while just sitting there quietly, I could change everyone's mood to happiness and laughter.

I realised there was something sinister and dangerous in what I was doing. Then one day (I can remember no precipitating circumstances at all) I changed five pounds into silver and pennies, went to the largest restaurant in town, ordered every dish on the menu and piled all the food up into a high tower on one plate. I went to the cash desk holding all the silver I had collected cupped in my hands and then let it stream out on to the hard floor in front of the desk. I went back home and remember digging up single plants from the flower beds and replanting them together in pairs.

My family soon heard independently of what had happened in the restaurant and sent for our doctor. I remember explaining at length that I was not responsible for what had happened, that there had been two vigilantes or masons there who had taken telepathic control over me and had forced me to act in the way I did.

I was sent to a large red-brick mental hospital far in the country surrounded by a high wall. The reception ward was outside the main gates, under the shadow of the wall. There were several nice young patients in the reception ward in the same sort of difficulty as I was. Then there were some terrible older patients looking like witches and ogres. I could see their psychic force as a horrible dark blue-mauve luminous shadow lurking around their heads. I thought that these people used psychic power to upset the vulnerable younger patients and that they made us behave as though we were mad.

I remember entreating and threatening these elderly people, and because I could not hope to compete with them on a psychic level, shouting at them to make them stop. I remember the lonely endless days in the padded cell and the continuous stench of the cell – rubber and stale vomit. If only I could have found somebody in authority whom I could have talked to, who would have been able to understand what was really going on. The early interviews I had with the doctors at the hospital stick hard in my memory. At this stage I was only too willing to tell my doctors everything – how my innocent experiments had opened Pandora's box into a world of supernatural frightfulness. I was willing to tell them everything I saw, felt and heard.

I remember the bewildered sadness of my parents visiting me. What could I say to them? How could they hope to understand?

I started slowly to learn the five basic rules of how not to appear insane. These I called my 'sanity rules'; the rules of how to get out. (1) Never mention any hallucinations you are having to anyone, not even your own friends and relatives. (2) Never transmit telepathically on any account. (3) Never talk about telepathy or psychic power to anyone. (4) Avoid fights and physical violence of any sort; (this was by no means easy in the type of ward I was in). (5) Most important rule of all – I had to secretly learn all I possibly could about defence against telepathy and psychic force in whatever form this might take.

There was plenty of opportunity to learn. Both in the ward and during the hour's break in the dusty exercise yard, there were any number of old inmates to be found blowing their psychic tops. The most important thing seemed to be to learn how to distinguish between thoughts from my own mind and dangerous thoughts and impulses put into my mind, either to throw me or to test my sanity.

I thought that if only I was left alone I would soon be fit enough to pass any sanity test going and walk out a free man. The trouble was the treatment I was receiving. The purpose of the treatment seemed obvious to me – my brain was to be so damaged that I would no longer be capable of receiving or transmitting telepathically. The treatment prescribed was massive ECT and 60 insulin shock comas. The actual treatment was horrible and frightening, impossible to evade or resist in any way. A refusal to take the morning injection meant being held still by two male nurses while a third male nurse punched my stomach.

I remember well after my first insulin shock coma talking to one of the other patients on the same treatment. The conversation went like this:

'I was told I was going to go to sleep after my injection and I would wake up two hours later feeling better. It wasn't like that at all. It seemed to go on for hours and hours and it was horrible.'

'That was your first go; you don't know anything yet. Just wait till you've got used to it, then you'll really know what it's like – it goes on for ever.'

'But it shouldn't be like that. I'm going to tell the doctor.'

'Don't be a bloody fool. You tell them that and they only increase the dose and that makes it worse.'

'But they've got to do something. I can't possibly go on like that for another five months.'

'Listen, you bloody fool, the boy before you, in the very same bed you're in now, wouldn't listen to sense and kept complaining about the treatment. First they increased his dose once, and when he went on complaining they increased it again. Then a few days later he was stone dead. We saw him carried out when we were all meant to be under. They'll tell you if you ask he's been transferred, but we know better.'

The effect of the treatment gradually filled me with despair. My memory was slowly being blanked out, but much more alarming was the slow onset of mental confusion. I would get up after treatment not knowing where I was, what time of day it was or who the people around me were. I found it increasingly difficult to hold myself together as a person and to retain what little insight into my condition I did have left.

I made complaints to my doctor about what was happening to me. He maintained that it was nothing to do with the treatment but was simply the natural progression of my particular illness, and the whole purpose of the treatment was to arrest the illness. I remember the empty feeling left by these short infrequent discussions and how hard I had to struggle to prevent myself from saying too much.

Between attacks

Towards the end of 1950 I went back to college, unable to remember the names of my tutors, remembering nothing of what I ever learnt there. Not only had my memory gone but the sharpness and speed of mind had gone as well. I had difficulty in organizing the simplest thought. Nothing in life made sense.

A year later my mother showed me a short letter sent to her by the hospital during my illness. The letter said that in their opinion there was no chance of my ever recovering sufficiently to allow my release from the hospital. In all her letters and visits no hint of this letter ever showed through the hope she tried so hard to give me.

Once out of hospital my problems with psychic forces became trivial. I thought I had built myself such an armoury of psychic defence through interaction with the high powered telepathic inmates of the hospital that any difficulty to be met with in the outside world must be absolutely child's play. All I had to do was to hold fast to my five rules and there would be nothing at all to worry about.

After graduating, I found I was unable to get a job. The University Appointments Board sent my name to dozens of employers, and I answered umpteen advertisements for university graduates. This was at a time when it was practically unheard of for students from my particular college not to get snapped up, even before graduation. Eventually, after months, I got one interview. The man who interviewed me said he had had a very good report about me from the Appointments Board. There was just one thing he wanted to ask me: 'It says you should have got a good first but because of an unfortunate breakdown and subsequent long illness you were only able to get a third. Would you mind telling me exactly what happened?' Needless to say, I did not get the job. After this I gave up all hope of getting a job through the University; I complained to my tutor about his reference: he said he could do no more. The college had, of course, to be fair to the employers as well as to its students. Anyway, the reference was confidential: who did I say was the employer who told me about it?

From then on I applied for jobs on the strength of my GCE and school reference. What had I been doing since then? Helping my father with his gardening business. (My father did not have a business.)

Once I got a job – and it was extremely easy to do so on my new qualifications! – everything went well. It seemed remarkably easy in just a few years to work up through the company – up to a certain point that is. It was even easier to apply from there for really good jobs citing my university degree but giving my firm as a reference. Only some of the jobs I applied for asked for university references; these I naturally didn't follow up. I was amazed to be showered with job offers; it seemed I could suddenly choose any job I wanted.

I was by now happily married. Four years after my illness I wrote to the hospital asking about marriage. I had a pleasant letter back saying that marriage was of course all right provided my future wife fully realised the risks involved. We settled down happily and started a family. There seemed to be not a care in the world.

Second breakdown

My rules of sanity served me well for about 13 years. Some of my former quickness of mind returned. I had several children, and was doing well as a middle executive in an American-owned company. Then at the beginning of 1963 I noticed something rather strange about the company I worked for – everyone apart from me seemed to take religion seriously. Not only practising religion but also actively spreading the word. Then I started getting the visions, beautiful visions of Christ, the Virgin Mary and gorgeous angels with beautiful wings beckoning me to join them. How was it done? Telepathy, of course, but done by trained professionals with nothing to show except perhaps the occasional taut, pointing fingers strained in my direction, or, turning quickly, I could interrupt the fixed stare into the back of my head.

Then I started seeing haloes; round the heads of religious statues, around the heads of nuns and clergymen, beautiful vivid blue haloes, even sometimes around the heads of pretty girls whom I never suspected of being good or Christian. But each time I had a vision it came with power, majesty and shock. How could anyone who was in the least bit aware avoid being spiritually dragged into the Church by such methods? Then I felt my head being turned, turned towards the churches; I would be drawn into the churches and my eyes would be directed to look at particular religious emblems within.

The religious drama (as I saw it) began to upset and disturb me. I decided to drop one and only one of my sanity rules. I would use telepathy to hit back. When I received a vision I would locate the source sending the vision and would transmit back, distorting the vision and making a nonsense of it. This seemed to me to have some effect. A large number of people at the office went off sick. There was whispered talk about evil spirits. I pretended naive incomprehension. The visions stopped.

Then came the turn of the screw, my young children. I thought I detected telepathy being used to take them out of my control.One instance was a family outing. My youngest son slipped away. I found him standing in terror on the edge of a parapet with a twenty foot drop in front. When I grabbed him from behind he seemed on the very point of jumping. I looked over the parapet to see a man with glowing eyes staring up; I heard a voice in my head say: 'You have been warned'. Another instance, my car had to stop at traffic lights and my daughter started screaming. I saw an old man peering into the car with blazing green eyes, staring at my daughter, using naked psychic force that I had not seen for 13 years. I got out of the car and shouted at the man and told him to clear off. My daughter did not stop screaming until I had returned home and put her to bed.

I told my wife what had happened and she replied that the only person disturbing the children was myself. A few days later the firm rang my wife and told her that I had been disturbing people at the office and should see a doctor. My wife managed to find the psychiatrist who had looked after me at my old hospital. He came to London especially to see me. He told me everything had changed in the last ten years. There was no longer any need to go to hospital. All I had to do now was to take pills he would prescribe and all would be well. I refused to take the pills because I thought that if I did I would no longer be able to protect my children.

Things rapidly went from bad to worse. When I was out with my children they would jay-walk out into the road in front of oncoming traffic. My eldest boy started waking up in the night screaming with terror, and, to me, showed signs of becoming autistic. I was unable to find what was influencing him but was informed by some of my friends that they had seen my son on several occasions talking to a strange man whom I was unable to find.

Then in the train on the way to work I sat opposite a girl with a spendid halo. She looked gently into my eyes and let me know by telepathy that I could commune with her. I started to rush through my mind all my troubles but she interrupted to tell me there was no need, she had already been briefed with my history. I told her I feared for the lives and sanity of my children and that I feared to leave home because of them. Her eyes suddenly became very piercing. She informed me that because of what I had done and was doing the only way I could possibly save the children was to leave them and go to hospital.

I asked her if I gave myself up and went to hospital, how could I possibly know that nothing would happen to my children? She gave me a radiant smile and promised in her official capacity as angel on behalf of the establishment that if I went to hospital my children would never again be endangered in this way. Still smiling, she got up, touched my outstretched hand for a second and left the train at the stop before my own. During this meeting, no actual word was spoken out loud by either of us.

At the office, I tidied my desk, said I was unwell and was going for a check-up. I went home, packed a case, and my wife drove with me to a hospital that had been highly recommended. Once there I asked to be admitted as a voluntary patient for observation only. I was told by the doctors that admission was sought by everyone as it was a very good hospital. They had a long waiting list so why should they admit me? I said I had promised to go to hospital for three days' observation and I wanted no treatment, so I would be no burden to them. They said that they certainly could not admit me on those grounds and what was more, no other hospital would, as there was a shortage of hospital beds. I told them my children were being menaced by psychic forces and I had to go to hospital to stop it happening. What did I mean by psychic forces? Well, everyone had what was known as a psychic balance. This could be disturbed by either being loaded with too much psyche – this could be seen by some as a blue, white or coloured radiance – or it could be disturbed by a withdrawal of psyche, visible to some as a black negative radiance. Once the balance of psyche was disturbed one became prey to all types of telepathic forces. Did I associate positive psyche with good and negative with evil? No, both positive and negative psyche could be used for the same ends.

My interview was very short. I had passed the entrance into the hospital with flying colours. The first three days there were quite enjoyable. I refused to take the assortment of coloured pills

I was always being offered. In my view, I was there as a voluntary patient for observation only. There was the open door to the street, the large pleasant garden, the pottery shed, the art room, the music room, the enjoyable relaxation classes, the interesting psychotherapy groups. What more could one want? I remember contributing to the large psychotherapy class. A girl had said that if only she had followed more closely the teaching of Jesus Christ she would not be in such a mess. I said that if Jesus Christ was alive today there would be no need at all for the Establishment to crucify him. Thanks to modern medical science he would be sent straight to a mental hospital like the rest of us and be either reduced to a cabbage or plugged into the national grid with ECT. Why did they think there were no political prisoners in Britain, only mental patients? I remember the tense silence after my remarks and the worried people coming up to me afterwards. What did I really mean by what I had said? Oh, nothing, forget it, I was only joking.

My first nights at the hospital were hell. I was in a room with three others. The young man next to me was a heroin addict trying to withdraw. His mind was full of creepy horror, and at night when I was trying to sleep I was quite unable to block out the penetration of his mind. Disgusting visions of living bodies torn open and riddled with writhing maggots and flukes. There was no chance of any sleep. And yet this young man was so quiet and pleasant and helpful. He said he did not dream at night, so I certainly was not getting the vibes from him.

Later he showed me his collection of paintings, work he had painted over the weeks he had been in hospital. I remember the shock I had looking at his paintings – the same vivid colours, the crawling maggots everywhere.

Then came the interview with the doctors. I had been there well over the three days I had promised to stay. I now wished to leave. I would have been happy to stay longer but I had constantly complained about the need to change my bedroom, and nothing had been done. I needed to go home to rest and sleep.

The doctor said that going home was out of the question. I was a very sick man, much sicker than I thought. It was essential for me to have medical treatment.

If I left of my own accord, I would be arrested immediately

and returned to hospital – not to the one I was in, but to an old country hospital like the one I was in before. I had to realise I was not only sick but also dangerous. But how could they say I was dangerous since I had never injured anyone in my whole life? The doctor said that I must know exactly what they meant. I was really much too sick to be at that hospital at all, and was privileged to be there. All right, I said, I would stay a few days longer but I would refuse medical treatment. After all, a man under sentence in prison had the right to refuse treatment, hadn't he?

How had I got into such a mess after what had happened before? What had happened to my rules of sanity? Why hadn't I stuck to them? What *were* my rules of sanity? I was so smashed out of my mind I could not remember them. All I remembered was that it was most important to put 'T' instead of the word 'telepathy', in case the rules were found by the wrong person. I remember sitting for hours trying to write out the rules. In the end, instead of just five rules I finished up with dozens, all on separate sheets of lavatory paper. I kept them in a wad in my pocket.

Second remission

I was eventually let out after about half a year, towards the end of 1963, on condition that I kept on taking the tranquillisers.

I went on taking tranquillisers for a year. My hallucinations certainly went, but my joy in living went as well, leaving only a death wish. I could no longer think clearly and quickly, which made my work impossibly difficult. I kept being transferred down to simpler work. Not only could I not think clearly but confusion seemed to be settling in permanently. It seemed I was on a one-way ride to accelerated senile dementia, or suicide.

After giving up tranquillisers the hallucinations and experiences of telepathy returned. But I still had my manual of sanity rules. If only I could keep to them all would surely be well.

Third breakdown

My next breakdown was four years later in 1967. There were two developments with which my sanity rules could not cope. First, I became aware of a voice in my head which told me what to do. Sometimes it was most useful, for instance knowing exactly where to find things I had lost. Sometimes it was impossible, making me buy things I didn't want or need, making me spend hours wandering the streets visiting churches. When I followed the voice I would have a splendid feeling of well-being. When I opposed the voice there would come sudden visions of terror. Second, I became convinced that I was being used in a sort of Royal Hunt of the Sun or telepathic fox hunt in which I always played the part of the fox against huge crowds of religious fanatics, the only weapon allowed by either side being psychic force.

The situation I have briefly described above was certainly worrying me and things were gradually getting worse, but things had often become worse than this before and then somehow had got better of their own accord, and I had been able to cope. So why suddenly did I have to drop my first basic sanity rule, never mention your hallucinations to anyone? I only wish I knew.

What I did was to tell my wife what was happening. I remember her sitting quietly in silence as I explained at length, she did not look at me but looked down at her feet. After I had finished, what did I expect? Sympathy, encouragement, support, I suppose. She left the room without saying a word. A little later I tried to find her to discuss what I had said, but she had shut herself in the bedroom and was urgently talking to one of her friends on the telephone, so I left it at that. I knew she could not be talking about what I had said to her as I had solemnly bound her to absolute secrecy.

Nevertheless, she had in fact telephoned the doctor. I did not realise this, even when he called ten minutes later, until he told me that he would like to arrange for me to go for not more than three days to a very good hospital he knew, not one I had been to before. For the first time, in a rush, I understood what was happening.

I was bewildered and ran up to the top room of the house and locked myself in. How could she do it? I remember looking down on the steady stream of invaders entering the house.

First, the unknown woman, a social worker, then the police car with lights flashing and the three policemen, then the ambulance with lights flashing and the two ambulance men.

I have never been able to accept what happened to me that

day; even now I cannot forgive it. My wife, in turn, cannot understand my unforgiveness.

I was sent under section to a psychiatric hospital. In the early hours of the first morning I managed to escape twice. The first time I was thrown by an enormous white cart horse I had tried to mount to get away on. The second time I reached, barefoot, a specialist cancer hospital. I remember telling the night duty man that I had recently made a generous gift by cheque to cancer relief (which I had done), so could he please lend me some old shoes and clothes in exchange? All I had on was cotton pyjama bottoms, and the early morning cold was biting right through me. My clothes had been taken away on arrival. I had had to use the towel I was issued with to fill out the bed so it looked as though it was still occupied.

I was returned to the psychiatric hospital, where I stayed about four months. I was started on long-acting tranquilliser injections. I refused to have any more injections as soon as I was released from hospital but I went on taking tranquilliser pills for nearly a year. I had to stop − the temptation to commit suicide was almost irresistible.

I spent hours on the roof of one high building looking down. Each time I went there the idea of jumping became easier. (I have never had the slightest desire to commit suicide at any time, except when on tranquillisers.)

Third remission

After the comparatively milder treatment I had received during my last stay in hospital, the fear of going into hospital and never getting out again was not worrying me as it had done previously. The problem now was essentially different. The remission time between breakdowns was getting shorter. If for no other reason than that I was unable to keep them, my manual of sanity rules was obviously inadequate, but the treatment I received each time I broke down seemed only to substitute a sort of progressive brain damage for a temporary loss of hallucinations. My chance of putting the manual right before I became a permanent inmate appeared remote.

Fourth breakdown

My next breakdown happened in 1969 two years after my

previous release. We had taken into our house a large stray semi-wild tom-cat. I felt a great bond of sympathy with the animal and I used to watch it mesmerise birds on the lawn so they were quite unable to escape or even move. I felt the cat becoming my familiar, and believed I could control its movements and even see through its eyes. Then one night the cat was nowhere to be found. Soon after going to bed I had a nightmare. I was in an iron cage seeing through the cat's eyes. A man with pliers was tearing out the cat's claws slowly one by one. I woke screaming only to see a giant, grotesque cat's head looking in through the window — so large it filled the whole window frame. I picked up the nearest heavy object, a wireless set, and threw it at the window, breaking it. The neighbours complained to the police about the noise, and (because of my record) I was sent back to my last hospital under a compulsory order.

It seemed obvious to me that the only chance I had of surviving was to learn to live with my hallucinations especially when they were at their worst, and the best place to do this was in the protected setting of a mental hospital. I therefore did not swallow any of the pills, but kept them in my mouth until the coast was clear, and then put them down a drain. As nurses are especially trained to watch out for this, it sometimes, but fortunately not often, meant holding tranquillisers in the mouth until after the sugar coating had gone; how bitter they were!

I had found by long experience that I could always cope with old hallucinations without giving away to anyone I was hallucinated, simply by bracing myself, by using very tight self-control, and because I had become familiar with them. It was the unexpected new type of experience which brought me down. The new problem this time was waking from a nightmare to a strongly-hallucinated reality, leaving me out of control.

I started using for the first time a new technique I had been reading about in my hunt through the libraries — this was called systematic desensitisation. It seemed to work remarkably well, and after the seventh nightmare I had organised perfect control on waking.

At the end of only a month in hospital I passed a medical review, was released from the compulsory order, and obtained my discharge. For me this was an astonishing all-time record.

Self help

It is now over five years since this last hospital stay. Since then I have been on the brink perhaps twice. But each time the loss of control has been smaller, the return to sanity more sure. I now feel quite confident that further breakdown is extremely unlikely, simply because if it comes again I now have all the experience and knowledge I need to deal with it myself.

Factors I believe are very important in obtaining my full recovery from schizophrenia are: having a psychiatrist in charge of my case to whom I could relate; also a long period of unemployment, without any effective pressure to get back into harness, is, in my opinion, essential to consolidate recovery. Straight back to work on tranquillisers after a breakdown is to my mind a sure road to further breakdown or suicide.

There is also another factor which may have helped recovery. In my burrowing through textbooks on mental illness, I did evolve an explanation which has been very helpful to me: the concept of the 'split brain'. This was an idea which I could fully appreciate and use to my advantage – unlike the concept of the split or fragmented mind which only made me confused. Whether other people would find it equally useful I don't know but it makes things much clearer to me.

Lastly I must mention the sympathy and support constantly obtained from other patients, many in a much worse plight than I was. One way in which patients are most unhelpful, however, is when they humour each other's hallucinations. If one man complains about seeing pink elephants and a second man agrees that they are there, the second man gains friendship and gratitude at the expense of the first man's grasp of reality.

Postscript

Having now read this account through several days later, I cannot but wonder at the pale shadow I have described as compared with the reality of schizophrenia and the way it is treated in this country.

In the first few pages I seem to have failed to show any of the sense of injustice I certainly still feel. I wanted to show that the punishment, or as it was euphemistically called, 'treatment', in no way fitted the 'crime', i.e. piling too much food on one plate.

One fact that should be quite obvious from what I have

written is that for the greater part of twenty-five years I have been living in the community while being classifiably schizophrenic; in that I was hallucinated (except for a few months when I was taking very heavy doses of tranquillisers) and I was also deluded, insofar as an active belief in the more exotic ramifications of telepathy (telepathic mind control, for example) is considered to be delusional. For the most part I achieved this freedom by relying on my manual of sanity rules which, in the first instance, were nothing more than a method of deceiving other people, including doctors, as to my state of mind. I don't think I am in any way exceptional in doing this. In hospital I constantly obtained the most helpful advice from other patients as to what to say and what not to say, and the sort of unexpected questions I would be likely to get from different doctors and how they should be answered. For example: 'Dr. A. is bound to ask "Do thoughts sometimes come into your head". All you need to answer is you're not sure exactly what he means. You must then sit tight and make certain you say nothing more during the next two minutes' silence.'

If I had not been able to rely on the apparent subterfuge of my sanity rules to get out, but had stayed behind to have my hallucinations and delusions completely cauterised out of my brain, I am personally convinced that I would not be now sitting here writing this – I would long ago have been reclassified as chronic and would have been hidden away out of view.

Learning to live with hallucinations certainly takes time, but once it has been learnt, life can still be lived to the full and enjoyed with little or no residual handicap. Having an active delusion about telepathy at the same time is certainly most unhelpful and greatly increases vulnerability. I only wish I had found at the outset an alternative philosophy like the idea of the split brain which I could have fully believed in.

Is there any difference between the idea of the split brain and the split mind? Many people who can no doubt easily imagine my mind being split or fragmented (and possibly even their own) will say I'm just splitting hairs. But to me, and I'm sure to very many people like me, the concept of my own mind being split, one part deceiving and confounding the other parts with hallucinations and terror, is totally inconceivable and unacceptable. My mind is mine absolutely and I can only think of it as being 100% for me at all times. It follows from this that my hallucinations are a threat from outside, that is from outside my mind. They must, therefore, be coming from the outside world, telepathy, God, etc.; or alternatively, as I think more likely now, from a part of my own brain which is no more part of my mind than, say, my little finger, though it is certainly part of me.

I have laboured this point at length in the hope that some of the effort that goes into the hopeless task of trying to convince people like me that our minds are split or fragmented, may be diverted to some more promising approach.

Do I at the moment believe in telepathy? I can honestly say I do not know, and without there being verifiable scientific proof I will never know. I know quite well that my brain is fully capable of hallucinating any amount of psychic experience for my mind to wonder about; it does so all the time, and this obviously makes it quite impossible for me to assess where my subjective world ends and objective reality begins.

I think it is also necessary to ask the same question the other way round. How can I be certain that I am hallucinating at all, that what I see when I hallucinate is not a deeper terrible reality of which only a few people are fully aware? I can answer this fairly easily. Fortunately the part of my brain which produces telepathic hallucinations is not so clever, when compared with my mind, and sometimes, though not very often, I have been able to catch it out.

To give an example, up to a few years ago, I believed I could release a large charge of psychic force from my brain. I then found that with certain colour television sets (but by no means all), especially those with a certain type of indoor aerial, I seemed to be able to make them flash colours and go on the blink simply by releasing a charge of psychic force at them. At the time this seemed to me to offer a direct verifiable link between my supernatural world and reality. There was a shop with a colour television set in the window not far from where I worked, and I used to spend long periods in front of this window experimenting, apparently making the set flash, pulsate and blink just at will. An instinctive feeling warned me very strongly that what I was doing was wrong and could lead to danger. A couple of years earlier I would have obeyed this instinct and left it at that, but I had started systematic deconditioning since then, and I felt that I would be able to cope with any eventuality. What I wanted to do was to make the television set flash red, blue or green as I chose. Instead I found, to my great surprise and after a lot of research, that my releasing of a psychic charge was almost entirely involuntary. There were long periods when I just could not do it and others when I could not hold back. I eventually found the whole secret. I could only release energy when a car or lorry was passing which had faulty suppression on its ignition! So I finally recognised that I had no telepathic powers after all.

How do I know now I am entirely out of the woods, that some new development will not take place which will reconvert my agnostic world into one of terrible para-normal reality? The answer is I don't; in fact, going by past performance I am pretty certain it will happen again, but I am not in the least bit worried since I now know how to cope. I will be able to use systematic deconditioning to take away the terror from the new situation, and once the terror has gone out of my hallucinations my world will quickly return to normality, so quickly, in fact, that very few, if any, people will realise there is anything amiss.

I do not now think of systematic desensitisation (or systematic deconditioning as I like to think of it), as being in any way a kind of magic talisman or ritual. I think of it as an essential natural technique for survival that almost everyone has learnt without need of teaching. People do it automatically when they sit back, relax and go through in their minds any events of their day which may have worried them. I think there are just a few unfortunate people like me, who, for some reason or other, never acquired the art of deconditioning naturally and so we have to learn it systematically.

When applying systematic ||| deconditioning to my hallucinations, all I did was to sit down, relax completely (as I had been taught previously in hospital), and then run through in my mind all the hallucinations that were worrying me in increasing order of terror. As soon as I found myself tightening up I would stop, re-relax, and go back to the beginning, starting again with the least frightening hallucination. Once I had mastered hallucinations in this way I was able to use the system for coming to terms with many things that had up to then worried me in real life; crowds of people running, for example, and people shouting at me.

How is it possible to get someone who is lost in their own world to take up systematic deconditioning seriously? I think in many cases it should be quite easy, provided it can be tailored to fit their private world. When I took up deconditioning I was hopelessly deluded and hallucinated. I saw systematic deconditioning as one possible defence system against the myriad psychic forces of my enemies.

The part of the above story I found hardest to write was the interaction with my wife just before my third hospitalisation. Why did I have to write it? Because it is something that should never, never have happened. I certainly don't mean by this that there are never times when people like me need to be taken away from their homes, if only as a protection for their home and family. It is how it is done that is all-important. If only there could have been some subterfuge which I could have found convincing; for example, if the doctor had apparently called to see my wife and then, as if by accident, had found that I needed help (while my wife pretended that I need not go to hospital). Surely there must have been some way to have managed it better?

Since changes in the 1959 Mental Health Act are now being considered, I suggest the law should be changed so as to make it explicitly clear that doctors cannot prescribe medical, physical or surgical treatment without a patient's informed and continuing consent, even if he or she is under a compulsory order. Then mental hospitals could become the havens of rest, recuperation and re-education so badly needed for short periods by many thousands of people like me. At the moment they are for many of us places of terror to be fled from and they will remain so until the law is changed.

I have written this account as a success story, which indeed it is to me, and have throughout seemed to attribute nearly all the credit to myself. I have made only brief mention of the psychiatrist who brought me through my last two hospitalisations and who for nearly three years after the last one gave me endless encouragement as an out-patient.

I've said nothing so far about my family's problem of living with schizophrenia. The way we have coped is always to deny the problem's existence. Every family's problem is different, but in our own case, with children growing up in a close village-type community, I think the way we chose to ignore the problem made a great deal of sense. All leading questions, even those made out of sympathy, were dealt with in the same way — a long, deliberate embarrassing silence followed by a friendly change of subject. I have no idea, and equally no interest, as to how many of my friends and acquaintances know or don't know, since by tacit agreement the subject is never raised. We have always been pleasantly surprised to find how short a community's memory really is when the appetite for gossip is never whetted. My eldest children have been told about my illness but, happily, seem very little concerned.

One last remark — there is a final stage of recovery from schizophrenia when the ex-sufferer knows for certain that his worries are over, knows that however great the stress he/she is placed under, there will be no chance of further breakdown. Is this a rational belief or simply a delusion? In my case I had to prove it. I changed my job to what was for me the most stressful work I could imagine. I seemed to have no difficulty holding down this job although I witnessed some of my colleagues collapsing under the stress.

As in dreams

I feel that this description will be unsatisfactory mainly because of the need to condense. I talked to a group of doctors of my personal experiences after the first acute attack and it took me two hours.

I have thought of writing a book which I would call 'As in Dreams'. Many of the experiences are similar to dreaming, while in a waking state, and in dreams one can weep, or laugh, or cry out to experiences which are totally real. To me schizophrenia has been a mass of changing physical experiences, and sensations, and day dreams progressing to dominant thoughts and finally a voice. My thoughts were part wish fulfilling, part fear fulfilling, and centred largely on religion, in my first attack, and sex and religion in the second attack.

In conversation with other people with schizophrenia, while in hospital, they have agreed that while one is experiencing dominant thoughts or a voice these thoughts are totally and utterly true. Nothing can shake you on this. I took my treatment because the early Christians went cheerfully to the lions. I had to allow similar things to happen to me. I think that the only appeal that might have worked with me would have been that treatment might make me feel better and might enable me to think better. Certainly there would have been no strength in the appeal that treatment would get rid of my thoughts. I have continued to take treatment and now would be afraid to be without it. I stopped taking chlorpromazine after 5 years because, early on, the psychiatrist had suggested this might be possible. My second acute attack occurred nine months later and ended with compulsory emergency admission to hospital for the second time in my life.

My first acute attack came when I was forty and I was totally unprepared for it. Nothing in my medical training was of assistance in maintaining insight or in helping me to describe my experiences.

In retrospect my schizophrenic experiences started when I was about eleven. I had a few brief incidents of thoughts like a tape-recording being played in my head, of almost seeing my thoughts, and bizarre physical sensations. (These foreshadowed the first acute episode in 1966 when I was forty.) Then at sixteen years my academic performance fell off but this was not apparent to anyone but myself and I felt very guilty about it.

At twenty-three, in the final year medicine, I experienced two sudden concurrent changes which lasted until very recently. My vision altered but it is difficult to explain in what way. My visual acuity remained good but it was as if I had lost contact with reality. However hard I looked it was as if I was looking through a day dream and the mass of detail, such as the pattern on a carpet, became lost. The other change I can only describe as a genital sexual irritation from which there was no peace and no relief. The years between twenty-three and forty were ones of fear, guilt, inability to concentrate, failure of technical memory which made work very difficult, and progressively dominant thoughts. There were two realities: the world in which I lived and my day dreams, and the latter were more real.

Both my acute episodes were ushered in by the knowledge that I had been communicated with by God. In 1966, in Paris, I had a vision. The whole of my visual field was filled with a brilliant green, I saw the Cross, and then God spoke to me. With this certainty my thoughts then took control. They were religious thoughts very largely and I began to hear an intermittent voice. Just prior to my acute admission I announced to my aged father, who was in bed, that Satan in the form of the Loch Ness Monster was going to land on the lawn and do for us if we both remained together in the house. By this time, I heard the voice pretty constantly. A few days later at the time of hospital admission I had my third and fourth types of hallucination – of limb sensations and of smell.

I was in hospital one month and had ECT and chlorpromazine. My impression was the ECT did not make much difference but that chlorpromazine partially tamed my wild thoughts. The voice continued for four months. One day I was sitting listening to it when it suddenly said the equivalent of 'This is the final transmission: over, and out'. I have never heard it since. How did the voice know that it would never come again in spite of a second acute episode?

After eight months I was back at work but was functioning poorly. I still had dominant thoughts. My memory was appalling – I could sit for hours rereading something and still have no idea of what it was about. I would sit in committees forgetting the beginning of a sentence while the speaker was only half way through it. Roads that I travelled routinely created no detailed image in my mind. It was a slow process of two steps forward and one back.

For two to three years during and after the acute episode I lost the sensations of sexual irritation and was almost unaware that I had an appendage. The second acute attack was ushered in by intense burning fire-points of genital irritation and, at the same time the certainty that someone, who was mentally retarded, would know that he was being communicated with. Again, from that time on my thoughts took control. It was a period of wildly erotic sensations, lack of sleep, being out walking at any time from 1.00 a.m. onwards, marked tiredness, and frequent ideas of reference. Messages were being transmitted by car registration numbers and many written sentences had messages hidden in them in code. There were frequent certainties about heaven and its erotic nature.

Certain incidents, often isolated incidents, appear to have conspired against me at different times. I was pondering heaven and who would get there. In heaven we would all be the same and all young. There would be no parents and no children. I decided to set my parents, who were both dead, free to be young again. I went to the family graveyard and found a not insignificant hole in the ground. In mediaeval times there was the belief that graves opened and spirits escaped. The effect this had will be understandable.

At the time of my second compulsory admission I was defending some basic principles. I cannot fully remember what they were, but I think they were the basic constituents of heaven – courage and love, beauty and truth, challenge and hope, and pleasure. At the time I was sitting naked at the top of the stairs in my sister's house talking to two ambulance men while at the foot of the stairs were a mental welfare officer and six policemen. Outside were an ambulance and three police cars. The second acute attack was not so intense and not so prolonged as the first one and I had more awareness of what was happening to me. I was back at work sooner and lost ideas of reference and dominant thoughts quicker. However, the last two years have been ones of progressive physical discomfort and pain for which no diagnosis has been made. But I no longer believe, as I once would have done, that I am being manipulated by God, T.V., atom bombs or whatever.

Hospitalisation, when I was completely with the fairies, was I suppose necessary. I felt that to a certain extent I was being hospitalised because I did not conform and not because I was a danger to myself or to anyone else. When I was acutely ill, hospital was not as beneficial to me as when I was less acutely ill. Then it took the pressures off. I have derived considerable help from talking to other patients who have shared experiences. This was much more beneficial than group therapy with staff, or with relatives, who through no fault of their own cannot really comprehend.

Drug therapy has been varied. I have used chlorpromazine, thioridazine, trifluoperazine and pimozide. Pimozide was of no effect in this acute stage. Chlorpromazine seems to be beneficial with physical symptoms but trifluoperazine better with dominant thoughts and ideas of reference. I take these two at present.

Why one should suffer from schizophrenia I have no idea but I presume it is a biochemical disturbance. When one hears a voice it is almost as if this is a chemical overspill into the auditory pathway. Schizophrenia is defined as hallucinations without loss of consciousness. But, in my experience, I think that the prime effect is one of sensory deprivation. Schizophrenia-like manifestations can be produced in normal people by shutting them in a totally dark sound-proof room and leaving them alone. When I have schizophrenia episodes, which I do briefly, I fail to hear clocks ticking, I do not feel old floor-boards moving or hear them creaking when I should, and my visual awareness fails. It seems that my awareness turns round and looks into the gloom of my skull.

I find it diffcult to communicate my experiences even to doctors. When I tell them that I can't walk very far because the arteries in my leg are furred up they cotton on immediately. When I tell them about my deafness there is less understanding and possibly comments such as, 'It must be difficult for you'. When I tell them that I suffer from schizophrenia I often get blank looks and sometimes a wary one. *I have often felt that the mad cannot explain and the sane cannot comprehend.*

You cry as if you are appealing to the Lord for help

In the first instance I began losing confidence at work and people kept telling me to jump out of it. This I could not do apparently. Depression was coming on and eventually I found myself at home with the doctor treating me for stomach trouble. At this time I experienced a vision of an angel and at that moment the vicar of the church I was attending gave me Communion.

I must have recovered sufficiently for me to be taken to my mother's home in the Midlands, not very far away. Whilst there I was taken to bed and the family doctor came and he called for a specialist psychiatrist from the local mental hospital nearby and it was decided by my brother that I should agree to have ECT treatment in the hospital.

I was an inpatient for about five months with a break for Christmas and was given insulin and put into a coma. I understand that was to give me a boost. After coming out of hospital I paid regular visits for ECT. After finishing ECT I have been having chlorpromazine and amitriptyline tablets as medication.

Since 1956, when I first went into hospital, I haven't been able to keep a job for any length of time. For periods I was affected with continual shaking of the body and then attacks of not being able to control myself. This was probably the worst part of the illness and I turned against my wife and God. Slow motivation has occurred combined with deep depression which has prevented me from working on the local park where I have had a job since 1970. In the depression you cry as if you are appealing to the Lord for help. Other experiences have been a lack of synchronisation in the body which apparently is due to a mental blockage; also a lack of balance with tensions pulling your head backwards and forwards and this happens when walking. There is also apathy and slothfulness and, of course, lack of confidence. There is a nerve which causes frustration, which you feel moving with the tensions, which sometimes you feel in your mouth although they are apparently in the head. You do worry a great deal about things which other people take for granted. You take notice of what everybody says and, of course, you get very confused.

Two sides of myself

Editor's note
The following essay was written and sent to the editor after the author had begun to relapse and had wrongly come to believe that her former psychiatric adviser was dead. She was admitted to hospital within a few days of writing it and recovered rapidly. Three weeks later she could not remember what she had written. She was shown her manuscript and decided to write a commentary on it. We therefore have two documents, one written mainly from the inside, the other written partly from outside the experience of schizophrenia, by someone who has been trained both as a nurse and as a social worker.

Inside the schizophrenic experience
It is not easy to describe what it feels like to be schizophrenic and in fact it is not an idea that I entirely subscribe to, for although

diagnosed and treated by well qualified psychiatrists I still wonder if I am not really the victim of an organisation whose laws mankind cannot yet understand? I suppose it all began with 'the rats' and I can vividly recall the horror of knowing that one was lodged in my throat. Looking back, I can see that it was an illness, but that is the only part that I really can see as 'ill'; all the rest is just a jumble of experiences which make me doubt my very existence and identity, and confuse me as I have never been confused before.

Even now I am not sure what the rat represented. Perhaps it was a bad part of myself that I had split off and projected and which became imagined as a verminous creature threatening to choke me, rather than the poisonous part of myself which I was terrified of being engulfed by? But I can distinctly remember the horror of being choked alive, the taste of decay in my mouth as its body disintegrated inside me, and the deafness which I thought was being caused by its tail blocking my eustachian tube. Yes, now I can see that I was ill, but this does not help me to gain insight into certain other thoughts I have at present, which I am told are equally false. If anything, it makes the complex task of distinguishing fantasy from reality even more difficult.

It must have been just prior to the rat that the voices came and that I first began to realise what was happening to me. A few years earlier I had been doing midwifery training in a northern hospital and had delivered a baby which was anencephalic. * Due to shortage of staff, I was alone in the labour ward at the time. I was shocked at making the discovery and possibly somewhat relieved when the baby was born showing no signs of life. It was a large teaching hospital and such a congenital deformity provoked considerable interest, but no-one at any time suggested that I might have killed the child or that I had denied it life by not attempting resuscitation. Although saddened by the incident, it gradually became filed away in my memory and it was two years before I thought of it again. I was in a shop choosing a pair of shoes when I suddenly noticed the assistant pointing at me. To my horror I heard her telling a male customer

---

* Anencephaly: An abnormality of the brain which almost always results in the baby being born dead or dying shortly after birth.

that I was responsible for killing a baby and as the days passed I seemed unable to get their voices out of my ears. They are with me still, accusing, mocking, laughing, commenting on my every action and continually demanding my life in exchange for that of the baby that they believe I killed. To begin with I was terrified and yet too guilt-ridden to share my fears with friends. I contacted the police but they only 'humoured me'. I talked to my doctor but she said that it was 'my imagination'. Eventually she referred me to a psychiatrist, but by that time I knew more about the people who were hunting me and in a strange way this made me less afraid.

One has only to open a daily paper to find that a new 'pressure group' has been formed or that another band of people are busy campaigning for their rights and it seems that yet another movement is afoot aimed at recognising the plight of 'the stillborn'. Yes, even I find that idea quite difficult to conceive, but experience over the years has proved it to be a reality and has shown me that I am not the only person to be persecuted by them. The people involved are called 'Phenylists' and their policy appears to be that of 'a life for a life' and they currently want my life in payment for that child whom I failed to save. It amounts to murder, but there is a subtle difference, for their methods ensure a body but no trial and the only weapons used are those designed to break the mind, to confuse and distress until the victim eventually takes his own life as a means of escape. It is both subtle and effective and no questions get asked, that is not unless I can convince other people of my experiences, but this is difficult, as I have no concrete evidence and therefore they insist that I must be ill. But it is too logical, too formalised, to be a disease, and even if I were prepared to acknowledge it as such it would in no way help me to cope with my distress, but would leave me feeling completely helpless and distraught. At least now, knowing the rationale behind the scheme, I can plan my own defence and hopefully preserve myself intact against its violence. But one is fighting alone, never really being able to identify one's enemies and never entirely sure that a friend or relative is not included in this group.

I suppose that outwardly I do acknowledge that I am ill in so far as I attend a psychiatric out-patient clinic and until recently I took regular medication. But to me this is a charade that I submit to mainly for the benefit of others — for my employers who would be worried if I were left 'untreated', for my friends who feel that the medication 'calms me down', even for my doctors who perhaps genuinely want to relieve my distress, and who therefore provide me with a diagnosis because they have nothing else to offer as a solution. There are times when one even wonders if the doctors are part of 'the system'.

Until last year I was treated by a consultant for whom I had the greatest respect. He too saw me as 'sick', but while he refused to collude with my beliefs he nevertheless left me feeling that he was 'with me' in my experiences and appreciated my distress. We had endless arguments over drugs, and I was always afraid to relate to him too deeply, but he demonstrated his caring non-verbally — the Saturday visit when I was particularly upset, the hand on my shoulder as I left the consulting room, the proffered handkerchief when I was trying not to cry. Somehow he gave me strength when my own seemed insufficient and I was deeply shocked to learn a few months ago that he was dead. Initially I had a sort of dream in which I saw him kill himself, and then later I heard the nurses gossiping in outpatients' and planning to order a wreath. Even I was doubtful as to the validity of my dream but I would have thought that the comments of the nursing staff stood as reliable evidence, but when I questioned the medical staff about this tragedy, all knowledge of it was completely denied. What confused me even more was that one consultant, after telling me that the doctor in question died of a head injury, later denied all knowledge of this conversation. As a patient I felt obliged to bow to his greater wisdom, but as a human being I felt angry and bewildered at being unable to recall this event to his mind and I couldn't help wondering if he was deliberately trying to confuse me? Perhaps he, too, for all his kindness, is really working for them and maybe obtaining his gratifications by deliberately destroying those he is employed to help? This view would certainly support the way in which 'the system' operates, providing not only for the victim who ultimately kills himself but also for 'the helped who is ultimately destroyed by the helper'. I am sure that there are few psychiatrists who would subscribe to these goals but the idea cannot be discarded and I feel that this was why my own consultant chose to kill himself, because he too had fallen prey to their demands and chose to die rather than be compromised into destroying his patients.

It is a well known fact that medical personnel dislike treating their colleagues, they identify too readily with the situation and their fear is often demonstrated in punitive ways when their less fortunate colleagues end up on the wrong side of the sheets! Therefore as a trained nurse I was prepared to find hospital admission a somewhat uncomfortable experience, but I can honestly say that my only experiences have been good ones and that by the nursing staff I have never been treated with anything but kindness and compassion. Of course there has been the odd exception, like the ward sister who called down the corridor on my compulsory admission 'you'll never manage to kill yourself here'. She need not have worried as I had no intention of trying any such feat. Two weeks earlier I had found a piece of paper telling me that by killing myself I could atone for my sins and bring life to stillborn babies like the one I had killed. Consequently I had something of a 'messiah' complex and nothing less than a dive from a high rise building would do. Drowning in the bath or hanging myself in the toilet were just not on; I had something far more great and glorious in mind! But this apart, the nurses were consistently helpful and understanding, often possessing a sensitivity and awareness that was not evident in the psychiatrists. Perhaps I expect too much, but I can remember being angry with the doctor who refused to look down my throat, saying that the rat was too far down for him to see, and with the one who prescribed chlorpromazine when my mind was really thinking more in terms of rat poison. It seems funny now, but at the time I would have been grateful if they had stated quite plainly that they did not believe that there was a rat in my throat. I was frightened enough, and their verbal assent to my symptoms yet refusal to act on them constructively, confused and upset me. I was angry also with the insensitive doctor who thought his M.D. gave him a 'divine right' to view my body and was totally unsympathetic to my shyness. Perhaps he wouldn't have felt so cocky if I had been the nurse preparing to do his blanket bath? It upset me also when one registrar wrote 'not very well informed' on my case notes after I had failed to remember the capital of Turkey and deliberately left my vocabulary test incomplete. He was unable to see that I was frightened of disclosing too much of myself, and that my illness had already placed me in a vulnerable position careerwise. For all I knew he might give me a low IQ and write to tell my college that I was 'too unintelligent to continue training'. I remember the same doctor impressing on me the need for patient identification to such a degree that I failed to prevent a fellow patient from shoplifting for fear that he would again say that I was adopting a professional role. I never forgave myself for this, and at that point determined to fight whatever obstacles came my way in order to preserve my identity and personal wholeness. Perhaps it is ironic that since then most of these obstacles have been psychiatrists.

It is one thing to be a nurse, but entirely another to be a patient. Often in my professional role both as a nurse, and more recently as a social worker, I have worked on wards of disturbed patients or with clients given to 'acting out' or violent outbursts, and while I have sometimes felt distinctly uncomfortable, I have never felt myself not to be in control. But when resident on a ward with disturbed and sometimes violent patients I have lived in a kind of fear, which although sympathised with by medical staff is not appreciated fully as they themselves are in positions of authority and can walk away from the situation at the end of a shift. I can remember three almost sleepless nights caused by overhearing that a male patient had a gun in a suitcase and the fact that I was not allowed to lock my bedroom door, and similarly I bore the scars for weeks of bruises received by restraining patients in a violent fight one breakfast time. I see the instigator of the fight in 'outpatients' from time to time and although he looks quite 'meek and mild' I still cannot refrain from giving him a wide berth!

If the nurse/patient roles do not mix then the patient/social worker ones are even more ludicrous. I can never quite make up my mind if people go into social work to take their minds off their problems or whether they inherit the problems with the job, but there is something slightly amusing about a social worker who develops a psychiatric illness. One's colleagues tend to regard it with a 'if you can't beat them, join them' type of approach, but I think the real reason is that the role carries with it an assumed inner strength and clarity of perception which others find hard to comprehend when it breaks down. Nurses also appear confused by this complete role reversal and psychiatrists are continually on their guard against the social workers' use of interpretation and each party becomes exceedingly anxious about being subtly manipulated by the other. I sometimes wish that we could forget our professional techniques and relate simply as human beings with the implicit acknowledgement of our human weaknesses, but perhaps in that position we would feel far too vulnerable.

The authority carried by the psychiatrist can be another stumbling block dependent on the individual personality. It can be inhibiting, destructive and frightening, or protective, creative and enabling, depending on its usage. Being scheduled under the Mental Health Act was one of the most frightening experiences of my life, yet the psychiatrist involved used it to promote every aspect of my mental well being and I look back to that time with gratitude for the care that he demonstrated in protecting me from myself. Yet frequently as a social worker I have found 'sections' being signed more for the benefit of the workers involved than for the patients; drugs being used not in a therapeutic sense, but so that the nursing staff could have some 'peace and quiet', and compulsory admissions being handled in the most frightening ways, or by resorting to subterfuge, like the G.P. who telephoned me last week asking if I could persuade a client to enter a mental hospital by telling her that it was a convalescent home. I myself have been fortunate in being treated at a hospital with excellent facilities and standards of care but there are many institutions in existence where care is unwittingly destructive and where clients are manifestly too ill-placed to campaign for better conditions and a more sympathetic approach to their condition.

One would assume that one would need to come to terms with one's own unresolved conflicts about one's illness before one is able to help others. But schizophrenia is such a blanket term and so frequently misapplied that I do not find this so and it is interesting that although there are many questions in my mind regarding the validity of my own schizophrenic experiences I have no doubt that my clients are suffering from a definite disease. My first schizophrenic client was called George and believed he was 'God' on the basis that he had been to both heaven and hell. He was always strangely reluctant to discuss the latter place but was quite eloquent with regard to heaven, which he described as 'full of dancing girls'. His delusions allowed him to fantasise experiences which he would never have dared participate in reality, and as they appeared to bring him pleasure rather than distress one was almost reluctant to rid him of them. On a reality basis life had little to offer George and it seemed that he had taken refuge in this world of madness and woven a rich tapestry of phantasy on a canvas of life that would otherwise have been almost bare.

Margaret was different again, terrified of the men who lived behind the pipes in the kitchen wall and who interfered with her body at night, and Peggy's diagnosis was presumably made largely on the basis of her chronically institutionalized and a-social personality. Neither of these latter clients were articulate or intelligent and it is for people like them that I decided to join the National Schizophrenia Fellowship. Personally I do not 'feel' schizophrenic and I would in any case find it extremely difficult to accept their help, but if I am schizophrenic then I am also fairly intelligent and articulate, and can therefore hope to help to determine the needs of my group and to campaign for legislation to meet these needs.

Although dealing with a fair number of schizophrenic clients I find that I do not readily identify with them and presumably this is largely due to the many forms which the disease can take. Also I have no special training in dealing with such clients and can only hope to provide warmth and sympathy; to feed back the reality of their situations and above all to demonstrate that I care deeply for them as individuals whatever their condition.

Even with fellow patients one does not find oneself swapping symptoms in the same way as one would if one had gallstones, and unless one is very sick one rapidly learns never to express any ideas which may seem 'odd', as it is better to live with one's fears rather than to risk the embarrassment of friends. At most one can only share with others the major areas of distress; the confusion, the fear that one is being overwhelmed by forces beyond one's control, the feelings of disintegration, the struggles to preserve one's identity at all costs. As a social worker I am able to help my clients with many of their practical difficulties but I am too embarrassed to ask for that help myself. Currently I am homeless and although it is an easy thing to pick up a telephone and book accommodation, I am too afraid of living alone in case of possible attack. It is something that friends and relatives and even perhaps my psychiatrist would not understand, and although I have shared accommodation with friends in the past, relationships pose a tremendous strain on me, and I am also afraid of burdening them by becoming 'ill'. It is things like this which make a professional life and schizophrenia so hard to bear. If I were unintelligent, inadequate, unable to work, there would be many agencies open to help me, but my professional role (and perhaps my pride!) exclude this help and I am sometimes too tired to want to carry on fighting any more. If I mention this to my doctor then he normally offers hospitalization as the only solution. But despite the good care, I feel that it offers me no real answers and I finish up doped with more sedatives than my body can accommodate and then organised into a flurry of group meetings and occupational therapy which even a person off medication would be hard pressed to keep pace with. If I can cope with this constant round of activity then I may as well be at the office coping with my own demanding job. I have no difficulty in managing my own daily routine but what I would welcome is some kind of 'crisis centre' where I could just 'flop' occasionally and let my illness wash over me. But then one can never be sure of emerging on the other side!

What then does schizophrenia mean to me? It means fatigue and confusion, it means trying to separate every experience into the real and the unreal and not sometimes being aware of where the edges overlap. It means trying to think straight when there is a maze of experiences getting in the way, and when thoughts are continually being sucked out of your head so that you become embarrassed to speak at meetings. It means feeling sometimes that you are inside your head and visualising yourself walking over your brain, or watching another girl wearing your clothes and carrying out actions as you think them. It means knowing that you are continually 'watched', that you can never succeed in life because the laws are all against you and knowing that your ultimate destruction is never far away. It means trying to work out if you are fit to be a social worker or if your perception of reality is so distorted that your clients may be endangered. It means over-working, being adequate is not enough, one needs to be exceptional so that no-one can attribute faulty work to your mental condition. It means desperately wanting someone to help you, to hold the bits of you together that you feel to be disintegrating, to be able to tell your psychiatrist the truth when most of the time you are lying because you feel that otherwise your liberty would be at stake. It means joking with a schizophrenic friend about her latest very serious overdose, and laughing hysterically over the nights I have spent sleeping rough, when all the time I know it was a frightening, miserably cold experience. It means being afraid to disclose your illness to relatives for fear they might be horrified or even use it as the reason for you not fulfilling their expectations of you.

To me schizophrenia means 'living a lie'. Outwardly being cheerful, smiling, resourceful, but creeping away at night to try and lose myself deep within my being. Knowing that I will be frightened sometimes beyond what I can bear, wondering how bad it will get, how long I will be able to work, knowing that soon one way or another it must end.

Another point of view

It is only a few weeks since I wrote down my feelings on schizophrenia but in that short space of time there have been dramatic changes within my life which have entirely altered my view of myself and my disease. When I originally recorded my thoughts I was quite seriously ill yet not fully aware of the fact or even prepared to acknowledge it. Now that I am 'well' again I can see my illness for what it was and I am more than a little embarrassed at the actions which it caused me to carry out.

To say that I no longer believe in what I wrote would be untrue because at the time my experiences were so real that they are hard to dismiss and as my illness tends to follow a repeating pattern I am fairly sure that one day these ideas will come back with renewed force. But at the moment at least I can see them simply as delusions of a very frightening kind.

A large part of my delusional system in my recent illness concerned the consultant whom I presumed to be dead and after receiving a letter from him assuring me to the contrary, I was equally convinced that an 'impostor' had taken his place. Prompted by this belief I went in search of this man to a northern city and spent considerable time informing police and other organisations of my suspicions. Eventually of course it was realised that I was sick and I was admitted to hospital. The first few days of my hospital admission are hazy; there was so much going on, so many voices mocking me and I was later told by fellow patients of my conviction that all the doctors were intent on killing not only me but them as well. I was hallucinating too; the rats came back, not in my throat this time but in my room, in my bed, and I grew frightened and disturbed. Fortunately appropriate medication made a dramatic difference and after a few days I was able to recognise my 'impostor consultant' as real and to gain some insight into what had been going on. Why my delusions should have taken this form is a mystery and can only be explained by interpretation. I had had a deep respect for the doctor in question and by moving from London he had effectively 'died for me' but how this had become so twisted in my mind I do not know.

Now that I am well again the seriousness of my illness alarms me and throws open the whole question of my future. I have been told that my illness is well encapsulated and that as I am normally able to distinguish the 'well' part of me from the 'ill' I am confident that it in no way affects my working capabilities as far as endangering other people are concerned. But are my employers going to be tolerant of a worker who occasionally has to have a few weeks in hospital? and how does it make me feel when colleagues (who do not know of my illness) or the mass media make jokes about the disease? The most famous I suppose is 'you're never alone with schizophrenia' and to my horror I can only think just how true that is. Also how do I feel when I get a circular on my desk warning social workers about parents who might potentially batter their children and finding that schizophrenic parents are set out as being a risk? Also what are my marriage prospects now? Can I accept that I would never be able to adopt a child or emigrate to America? And have you ever tried getting life insurance when you're schizophrenic? One can only learn to live with it and accept one's limitations.

Medication obviously plays a large part but somehow I think I prefer to be a little bit 'mad' than overdosed by major tranquillizers. In fact the whole question of medication raises for me a number of issues, for I am not only ill-adjusted to my disease, but often I am also loath to take the remedy. There is no easy answer to schizophrenia but there are various modern drugs available which can help sufferers over the 'florid' state of a schizophrenic breakdown and if taken regularly can make the chances of relapse more remote. But the side effects of these drugs vary enormously with individuals and perhaps I am unfortunate in feeling quite seriously affected, with symptoms ranging from a dry mouth and blurred vision to a terrible tension and restlessness and fears of 'losing myself' completely and being entirely controlled by the drugs. These feelings are often hard to appreciate and therefore doctors are inclined to prescribe medication without really being aware of the implications for the patient. Currently I am being urged to treat my illness 'as though it were diabetes'; that is, as an organic disease which can often partly be remedied by the continued use of a particular chemical compound, though diet, attitudes and social circumstances are also very important. This is certainly a view which makes schizophrenia sound more socially acceptable and is one which I can subscribe to quite readily when well. The problem lies in the fact that no sooner do I become mentally well than it appears foolish to continue taking drugs which make me feel physically unwell, with the result that I stop taking the medication and immediately begin to get ill again, often becoming so deeply enmeshed in my delusional experiences that the doctor's arguments for recommending the drugs have no real effect. Therefore the choice is only theoretically mine because I am often too ill to make the right decisions and these have to be taken for me in order to restore me from terrifying insanity to comparative normality. But the key lies in how I think of myself when I am well.

To be schizophrenic is best summed up in a repeating dream that I have had since childhood. In this dream I am lying on a beautiful sunlit beach but my body is in pieces. This fact causes me no concern until I realise that the tide is coming in and that I am unable to gather the parts of my dismembered body together to run away. The tide gets closer and just when I am on the point of drowning I wake up screaming in panic. This to me is what schizophrenia feels like; being fragmented in one's personality and constantly afraid that the tide of illness will completely cover me. I like to hope that one day medical science will find a permanent cure.

The story of my illness

Perhaps I had better tell the story from the beginning. At nineteen I was a wild boy at college, supposedly learning how to be a teacher. I went into boxing, being the protegé of an ex-professional. I would overdo the physical. I once challenged a fellow student to fight over a girl. I could not relate except in being 'harder' than anybody else.

When I finally got chucked out of college for not doing any preparation for school practice, I thought 'What shall I do now? Write?' But I knew in my heart it wouldn't work. When I got home, I said to my parents 'I don't want to be a bloody teacher'. My father said: 'Don't argue with him, he's not worth bothering about'.

Then I went to Woolworths as a trainee manager. My main interest was boxing. Everything I did, I overdid. I used to go for twelve mile runs, and read all night. My literary ambitions went into the background. I was more interested in fighting and drinking with the gang. I used to go to the most notorious pub in town and drink nine pints of rough cider every night. I was chasing after a girl who didn't want me. I would go round to the house of the girl and throw myself on my knees in front of her mother, demanding to see the girl. They would call the police, who would take me home. I fought with everybody who went out with this girl.

In four years I got through 30 jobs, anything from labouring to factory work, to office work, etcetera, etcetera. I got thrown out of the house for hitting my mother, and went to live in a flat. My last but one job was at the Ministry of Social Security where I hit a girl for spurning me.

I got in touch with a marriage bureau who put me onto a girl in Cheltenham. She jilted me, and out of my tears I prayed for the first time. Before, I was an atheist and a scoffer, but I found the faith that was to sustain me through eight years of illness.

In my flat, I began to get delusions. I was a storekeeper at the time. I wrote out 'Supreme New Plan', a system of life which I had worked out for myself. In it, I put 'Don't masturbate'. I wrote out notebooks full of plans. I kept thinking the Mafia were after me, and the F.B.I. were protecting me, ready to send me away to be trained. I kept thinking my parents were Jews. I would ask my landlady in my loneliness if I could watch their television and I would cry all the way through the programmes. Finally, I tried to get away to my Aunt Mary's: all I had with me was a suitcase with a bible in it. The police picked me up, and I made a false confession of murder so that they would incarcerate me and protect me from the Mafia. They told me to go home. Then I knocked the Vicar up at two in the morning for a talk. Next day he rang the doctor.

My doctor said I needed a rest. Sometime, next day, a medical superintendent and my mother came to certify me at the flat. A social worker took me to the hospital. I didn't resist; I thought it was all part of the plan. They put me in the locked ward, and the staff brutally beat me up. They put me on a section for a month. After three months treatment on drugs the hallucinations went, and my desire to hit women went; so they discharged me. There was no aftercare whatsoever; I didn't feel I could cope with a job.

I was in and out of the same hospital for six years. One year I spent in an anti-psychiatry community in London. My father decided to spare me the agonies of another 'Section 26' (a year's detention in a mental hospital), and took me from the locked ward to London. We lived in derelict houses, for which the landlord, another member of the community, charged exorbitant rents. But I was happy down there. The idea was to bring everything out into the open, and no drugs. I was thrown out of the community after a year for being violent. I was super-deluded and thought I was Christ.

For the past $2^1/_2$ years, I have been at a special psychiatric rehabilitation hospital. I'm sure this place can cure me, given time. The place is unique. I am in the clerical section. It's just like being at work. I want to write and, slowly but surely, my concentration improves as a result of the treatment here. I don't have delusions and hallucinations now.

The future of this hospital is in doubt, I have written to Barbara Castle about it with a petition of 70 patients' names. We are all praying for the future of our hospital.

Postscript

by John Pringle

These accounts of experiences with schizophrenia are of great medical interest but they are also aids to a more general understanding, bridges across the abyss of non-communication between ordinary life and the world in which the schizophrenia sufferer dwells.

Though not written for that purpose, they will be specially helpful to the relative who has the job of directly caring for a sufferer, either intermittently or continuously, and who wants to pick up any practical hints he can but may sometimes feel that the experts do not answer the questions he really wants answered, especially the simpler ones. To take a common behavioural pattern, relatives new to schizophrenia may be worried by curious grimaces, bizarre facial expressions, and strange muttering. 'What is she laughing about?' 'Who is she talking to?' they ask. A talk with doctor or nurse can explain the hold over the mind of obsessive thoughts and voices personalizing mysterious powers, but the explanation becomes more understandable after the accounts by our contributors of their hallucinatory and other experiences. Again, it is all too easy for the inexperienced onlooker to interpret the apathy or listlessness often met with in schizophrenia as having some tinge of deliberate or motivated laziness. But from the sufferers' descriptions it takes little imagination to guess at the sheer exhaustion induced by having to cope with different kinds of existence simultaneously, constantly having to try to adjust between the hallucinatory world and the world of what the rest of us know as common day. And even when the sufferer is free from a hallucinatory attack or other acute symptom one can see why adjustments to job-holding or other problems of 'ordinary living' tend to tire him far more quickly than the average person. The literature about the condition perhaps makes too little of the fact that it can be physically and mentally exhausting.

But before starting on the narratives the relative will have done well to absorb Professor Wing's introductory sketch which supplies the basic clinical background, and in a dispassionate way, clearing the ground of many myths and misconceptions.

There are weird details in these narratives which could make them an easy quarry for the way-out theorists about schizophrenia. Professor Wing considers some of these theories briefly and dismisses them. He sticks firmly to what is known and helps us to do the same. He points out that far more is known than is commonly supposed, that a considerable body of ascertained fact now exists, coherent with existing scientific knowledge, and that there is no need for us to be driven back on pseudo-mystical, political, magical, metaphysical or 'cult' explanations. He takes off the wrappings both from folk-lore and from spurious modern sensationalism. In a word, he is concerned to de-mystify schizophrenia.

This is surely the rational and sensible approach: to regard schizophrenia as a disability, a tragic one, one with unusual features, but not basically different from other crippling conditions. Further, the more matter-of-fact we can be in breaking down this disability into distinct components and tackling these separately the greater our probable success with it, provided we remember that we are dealing with a single individual, not the bits and pieces of one. The management of chronic schizophrenia, as Professor Wing agrees, is not mainly or even largely a medical problem. It is a social problem. One or two of the contributors describe adjustments they have personally worked out and clearly valuable insights can be and are achieved by some. But many if not most sufferers from the condition require help from others, which means society, and society in turn includes relatives, to do all that a concerned relative should do; general practitioners to provide advice, prescriptions for drugs and referrals to hospital; social workers to give support and various kinds of practical help; local authorities to maintain day-centres and hostels suited to those who find independent living a problem; voluntary caring agencies; Government departments concerned with financial entitlements, insurance and employment; hospitals to provide temporary shelter and treatment whenever life outside becomes too stressful.

This list is long – and could be extended – but each item corresponds to some specific need of the sufferer. The alternative to having such a comprehensive network would be to return all patients unable to live without special support back to psychiatric hospitals for an indefinite stay. Such a step would be regarded as cruel or indeed unthinkable because it would mean going back on the decision taken twenty years ago to run down the hospitals and embark on a policy of containing the maximum possible number of schizophrenia sufferers within the general community. But it is at this point that a strange confusion of aspiration and reality occurs in some quarters, giving an impression to those caught up in it of muddled thinking, if not double talk. The discharge of chronic schizophrenics is a fact. The run-down of long-stay hospitals is a fact. But in the experience of most relatives the community services which were planned as replacements are still largely an aspiration. The network of services we have outlined is an ideal. So far it exists hardly anywhere except in official literature and political speeches of a propaganda nature. But since present sufferers cannot exist on blue-prints, and life has to go on somehow, in practice, as the publications of the National Schizophrenia Fellowship and other surveys have shown, it is the relatives who are carrying most of the burden, or the sufferers themselves. Where a caring relative does not exist it is possible that some schizophrenia victims are actually worse off than they would have been in the days when long-term hospitalization was the rule. Many of the 'tramps' seen sleeping in parks or railway stations are schizophrenics and these do not seem to be obtaining much community care.

All this is depressing and was surely avoidable. It is hard to believe that the hospital service planners of twenty years ago seriously thought that local authorities would provide support services without far more money — and arm-twisting — from the centre than was actually applied, or that the highly conservative institutions and professions involved would stir themselves into unaccustomed working together without some miniature Beveridge revolution. As it is, the reader examining Professor Wing's description — it might almost be called a prescription — of the services ideally required — provision of a social environment which is adequately but not excessively stimulating, sufficient but not too vigorous rehabilitation procedures, carefully calculated adjustments of medication, and so on — may well ask *who* is to be responsible for each item in the programme, and *who* is to co-ordinate and supervise the whole. It would be nice to think that answers were being worked out, if slowly. But alas, it is still a matter of catch-as-catch-can. For want of anyone better, relatives, over and above learning to manage their patient the hard way, by trial and error, find themselves acting as unofficial liaison officers, arguing the need for a change of drugs, or a hostel place, or explaining to a social security office clerk what sort of disability the illness is. Relatives are very conscious that this is an amateurish, stop-gap way of carrying on. They would gladly stand down if anything better were offered. But no relative with experience of the appalling gaps in communication between different agencies, the hospital and local authority social workers who still do not seem to talk to each other, doctors who still tell relatives nothing, case-notes which still take weeks to travel a few miles between two hospitals – no such relative will easily be persuaded that even the embryo of a co-ordinated service is in existence.

So, in his or her own way, the relative can be, has to be, an unofficial, unrecognised, ancillary worker, a 'provider' of services instead of a 'consumer', which is the official fiction. There are other such fictions, including the legal-administrative one that *either* the sufferer is ill enough to be the subject of a compulsory detention order *or* he is totally fit to manage his own affairs in every respect. No 'in between' state is recognised as exists in real life. This means that the next-of-kin, or nearest responsible relative, need not be consulted either way, advised about treatment or after-care, need not be told anything at all, not even that a patient is being discharged and where to. The reality of course is that many chronic schizophrenia sufferers are not, and perhaps never can be, fully independent adults, able to fend for themselves, that they cannot survive for long outside some sheltered environment without breakdown unless a watchful eye is kept and tactful help is to hand. Sooner or later this truth will have to be admitted, and the present anomalies in law and administration put right. Meanwhile the National Schizophrenia Fellowship is pressing for the fact, emphasised in 'Schizophrenia at Home', that relatives are 'primary care agents' to be given official recognition. This would at least put the record straight and might have some educative value.

In the longer run, we would find it difficult to envisage some cases of chronic schizophrenia being looked after in the community at all except by a team, a team cutting across the present hospital/local authority/Government department functional boundaries. The members of such teams would be consciously and deliberately in touch with each other about each case, not tending to assume, as appears frequently to be the case at present, that if each professional worker performs adequately his role as 'hospital doctor', 'social security clerk', 'social worker' or what have you, the right thing will somehow get done. In such an ideal team any relative should be glad to play his modest part.

One small warning or qualification might be added to these narratives for the benefit of readers without personal experience of schizophrenia or of sufferers from it. In telling the story of our lives we all tend to remember the exciting moments, the peaks or troughs, the outstanding periods of happiness or wretchedness. So, very naturally, do these writers. They concentrate on what to them, and to us, are the interesting parts. But in chronic schizophrenia, as distinct from the acute syndrome, there are, so far as the outsider can judge, lengthy periods when nothing much is happening, and certainly nothing so lurid or bizarre as many of the experiences here recounted. Further, to the extent that our contributors are among the successes thrown up by the illness, having striven, as Professor Wing says, to find 'a way of life that is satisfying and useful', their accounts may not be wholly representative. For many chronic sufferers existence must present itself as a matter of long, grey stretches, without drama, and very rarely interrupted by extremes of terror or delusion. (Hallucinations, by the way, are by no means always experienced.) For these patients their characteristic preoccupations will be humdrum ones: being frightened of other people, frightened of themselves, being afraid to take a job, afraid that they won't keep it, afraid of other people's aggressiveness, afraid of their own, being bored and having nothing to do, running away from unwelcome people or difficult meetings, not answering official letters and then feeling guilty because they have failed, feeling guilty about their failures. All these are separate pieces of behaviour, individually trivial and occurring in most of us, but adding up to a comprehensive difficulty in coping with the small details of life, its rubs, frictions and petty problems. In between times they will also find consolation in talk or reading or going for a walk or listening to music.

Lastly, it should not need saying that the most perfect administrative clockwork can never be a substitute for person-to-person liking and concern. The schizophrenia sufferer may seem shut in upon himself, cut off from so many human contacts, at times even appearing positively to repel help or sympathy. But this is surface appearance only. Underneath is a human being aching to communicate or respond, if someone will help.

Further Reading

Brown, G. W., Bone, M., Dalison, B. and Wing, J. K. (1966). *Schizophrenia and Social Care.* London: Oxford University Press.

Emerson, J. and Wallace, C. M. (1969). *Schizophrenia: the Divided Mind.* London: B.M.A. and N.A.M.H.

Fish, F. J. (1962). *Schizophrenia.* Bristol: John Wright & Sons Ltd.

Iversen, L. L. and Rose, S. P. R. (Eds.) (1973). *Biochemistry and Mental Illness.* London: The Biochemical Society.

National Schizophrenia Fellowship (1974). *Living with Schizophrenia; by the Relatives.*

Snyder, S. (1975). *Drugs, Madness and the Brain.* London: Hart-Davis, MacGibbon.

Wing, J. G. (1975). Impairments in schizophrenia: a rational basis for social treatments. In: *Life History Research in Psychopathology, Vol. 4.* Eds.: Wirt, R. D., Winokur, G. and Roff, M. Minneapolis: Univ. of Minnesota Press.

Wing, J. K. and Brown, G. W. (1970). *Institutionalism and Schizophrenia.* London: Cambridge University Press.

FIVE The Changing Problem of the Treatment of Schizophrenia*
by Dr. Henry R. Rollin

WHEN I QUALIFIED, a person with schizophrenia (using the term as Bleuler intended it to be used, as a group of similar but by no means identical mental illnesses) admitted to a mental hospital for the first time had only a one in three chance of being discharged within two years, after which the hope of discharge withered with each passing year.

At this time, in the mid-thirties, psychiatry – or institutional psychiatry, to be precise – was somnolent if not fast asleep, a condition symbolised, and in some measure brought about, by the sedative drugs (paraldehyde and bromide, in particular), which were doled out by the bucketful.

In effect, mental hospitals were then closed institutions. The patients – a high percentage of whom suffered from schizophrenia and were in various stages of disintegration – were uniformly dressed in drab, ill-fitting suits or dresses, matched only by the drabness of their surroundings. Apple green and chocolate brown were the predominant colours in the decor, if such an elegant word is appropriate. The too-too solid furniture was adequate, but obviously designed for durability rather than comfort.

The nursing staff were in uniform; the women in starched dresses, aprons, and caps; the men in sombre dark suits, white shirts, and black ties, and, for outdoors, a military-type peaked cap. White coats, made-to-measure on the premises, were mandatory for all grades of medical staff except for the medical superintendent, who, as befitted an autocrat, could please himself.

The organisation of the mental hospitals was rigid and inflexible. Everything was done by the book of rules, and woe betide anyone who broke the rules. There was work for some of

---

* Reprinted with the permission of the *British Medical Journal*.

the patients – on the farm, in the immaculately kept gardens, in the laundries and kitchens, or in the various utility shops. But for the most part the insult of enforced idleness was added to the rest of the misfortunes suffered by the patients. This does not mean that there was any deliberate physical ill-treatment. There was not. The damage that was done was psychological. The attitudes and habits to which patients became accustomed over the years progressively reduced their chances of readapting to the needs of the greater community if and when they were discharged.

A more relaxed regimen

About this time, however, there were some indications of imminent changes. The Mental Treatment Act 1930 was enormously important in that it enabled persons suffering from mental illness to be admitted to mental hospitals on a temporary or voluntary basis, thus avoiding the lifelong stigma of certification. The inclusion of the word 'treatment' in the title of the Act was important too. Perhaps psychiatry was inspired by the epoch-making advances in treatment in general medicine, of which the use of the newly discovered drug Prontosil is a splendid example.

I remember working in Leicestershire as a locum in a small well-organised, run-of-the-mill mental hospital. I and a young whimsical Scot – whose Glasgow accent you could slice with a caber – were the only two resident doctors. There was no dispenser on the staff, so any dispensing was done by us. At dinner one evening my colleague suddenly announced, with all the passion of a divine revelation, that what our schizophrenics needed was 'not sedation, but stimulation.' We there and then made our way to the dispensary and concocted a mixture of tonics in two winchesters, one full-strength and the other half-strength. The first we labelled, in excruciating dog Latin, 'Mist omnibus robusta,' and the other, 'Mist omnibus lenta.' We then proceeded to reduce or omit the dose of bromide or paraldehyde prescribed for some of the patients with schizophrenia and to substitute one or other of our stimulating mixtures. The results were far from dramatic, but nevertheless apparent: there was less somnolence, and the stench of paraldehyde was certainly less pungent. My job finished some time later so that there was no follow-up as far as I was concerned – apart, that is, for an urgent request from my research co-worker for the precise ingredients of our mixtures, which, alas, I had forgotten. Our experiment reflected, perhaps, the current Zeitgeist. Throughout the civilised world the same stirrings were to be felt, although the means to the same end were infinitely more dramatic and in many ways far less innocuous.

Von Meduna, who was the first of what proved to be a veritable international brigade of workers, made his contribution in Budapest in 1934. He based his work on the premise, entirely false as it so happens, that epilepsy and catatonic schizophrenia were incompatible. Hence he argued that if artificial epileptiform convulsions could be induced in patients with schizophrenia the disease process, whatever that might be, would be attacked, or possibly eradicated. To this end, after a series of experiments on animals, convulsions were produced in patients by intramuscular injections of 25% camphor in oil. The results were variable, but the side effects – namely, delirium, prolonged vomiting, and pain at the site of the injection – were so unacceptable that this particular convulsant agent was abandoned. After further experiments, Von Meduna introduced leptazol (Cardiazol) as a safe and reliable agent.

Safe and reliable it may have been, but I can well remember the considerable reluctance of patients – no matter how psychotic they were – to continue treatment, so terror-stricken had they become during the preconvulsive period, a period for which no amnesia resulted. It became a matter in some cases of, 'first catch your patient.' Nevertheless, in 1937, Kennedy,[1] in a seminal paper based on the results of over a thousand selected cases so treated, maintained that there was a complete (sic) remission rate of over 70%, not including partial or 'social' remissions.

About this time, too, Sakel, following a series of hunches, used insulin hypoglycaemia in the treatment of schizophrenia in his Vienna clinic. The results were so favourable (apparently) that his method spread rapidly throughout Europe and America. Again, extravagant claims were made for its efficacy. Pullar Strecker[2] in 1938, for example, claimed that, 'Taking the spontaneous remission figures, we find that 23·6% of the total cases remitted, whereas practically double that number remitted

with insulin treatment.' He went on to say categorically, '...
Insulin therapy does constitute a decided advance in the
treatment of schizophrenia.'

Intense therapeutic activity

My personal experience with deep insulin therapy (DIT) began
after the war. I was responsible for setting up a clinic in my own
hospital after secondment to established clinics. A team of nurses
were trained for the far from simple, and at times, hazardous and
occasionally fatal, procedure. Staff morale was inordinately high:
we were doing real somatic doctoring and nursing. More than
that, we believed absolutely in the worthwhileness of what we
were doing despite the fact that some of our patients took on a
grotesque appearance as a result of weight they gained.

Italy came into the field in 1937. Cerletti and Bini first
introduced electric convulsion therapy (ECT) in 1937 for
treating schizophrenia. From about 1940 onwards papers
appeared in prestigious journals claiming success rates that
varied widely, but which were all decidedly encouraging – in
1943 Kalinowsky and Worthing,[3] for example, stated among
their conclusions: 'The rate of remission (recovered and much
improved) is 67·4% for cases of less than six months duration,
43·1% between six months and two years' duration, and 9·2%
in those of more than two years' duration.'

ECT in those early days was given 'straight' – that is, without
using relaxants and intravenous anaesthesia. A squad of trained
nurses attempted to reduce the effect of the violent spasm of
powerful muscles at the onset of the fit by applying pressure on
the shoulders, hips, and legs. Even so, dislocations and fractures
of the long bones and crush fractures of the lower dorsal and
lumbar vertebrae were not uncommon. Nevertheless, so
convinced were we of the efficacy of the treatment – particularly
of the acute phase of schizophrenia and for the 'maintenance' of
the chronic cases – that ECT clinics were the order of the day.
Clinics were held at least biweekly for from 20 to 30 cases.

To my mind the most regrettable innovation in the treatment
of schizophrenia was the blind, mutilating operation on the brain
– the so-called prefrontal leucotomy (or lobotomy), introduced
by Moniz in Portugal in 1936, and first performed in this

country at the Burden Institute, Bristol, in 1940. The protagonists of the operation were loud in its praise – Fleming,[4] for example, described prefrontal leucotomy as, 'one of the most startling of modern therapeutic procedures,' and sharply rebuked those who dared criticise it. 'There has been some hostile criticism of the operation by medical men with no experience of it and little experience of psychiatry,' Fleming thundered in the same paper. At the time of writing (May 1943), some 350 leucotomies had been performed in Great Britain and, in an analysis of 184 reported by seven authors, Fleming deduced that 72 were much improved and 44 improved. It is noteworthy that by 1963 the number of operations reported in Great Britain exceeded 15,000.[5] I confess that I was guilty of recommending the operation for 20 or so of my schizophrenic patients, and, may I add, nothing I have done weighs more heavily on my conscience.

It is as well to remember that at this time of intense therapeutic activity, which replaced the despairing nihilism of the 'twenties and before, prognostic optimism rode high. This coincided with a radical change in the ethos of the mental hospital. Little could be done about the buildings themselves, but the interiors were transformed by the introduction of attractive decorative schemes, modern furniture, and the like. The creature comforts were vastly improved so that the penurious, workhouse atmosphere was largely eradicated. Locked wards were, in the main, a thing of the past, so that security, if such were needed, became virtually impossible. The gibe, therefore, that doctors and nurses in mental hospitals were gaolers in white coats could no longer be applied. In all, the improved milieu in which schizophrenics were treated – an improvement that was to be later reflected in the community itself – must have had a positive effect on the prognosis, at least in social terms.

Nevertheless, as time went on, the scales of euphoria began to drop from our eyes and we were able to appraise, or reappraise, the advances in the physical methods of treating schizophrenics more clearly and rationally. As a result, Cardiazol was abandoned completely; the deep insulin therapy clinics were dismantled. ECT persisted, modified by relaxants and intravenous anaesthetics, and was used predominantly in the treatment of depression. The flood of prefrontal leucotomies was reduced to a trickle – those that were performed demanded much more precise techniques, and were carried out largely for conditions other than schizophrenia.

Pros and cons of drugs

Into the vacuum created by the disappointment with, and reduction in, the use of physical methods of treating schizophrenia, stepped the phenothiazines of which Largactil (chlorpromazine) was, and still is, the most important. Largactil was introduced into clinical psychiatry in 1952, since when there has been a constant stream of so-called psychotropic drugs coming off the pharmaceutical production lines.

Despite any reservations one may have, and I have plenty, there cannot be the slightest doubt that the introduction of these powerful drugs heralded the onset of a revolution in the treatment of schizophrenia. From a practical standpoint their main virtue is that they are easy to handle and may be administered by general practitioners in the home, or by psychiatrists in outpatient or psychiatric units attached to general hospitals. If admission to a mental hospital is necessary, the stay there may be measured in weeks rather than months, although shortness of stay may not in itself be a reliable guide to the long-term prognosis. Nevertheless, their usefulness in aborting an acute episode of the illness seems undoubted. Their efficacy, however, in chronic schizophrenia – and it is estimated that one-third of all cases become chronic – is more debatable. It could be that in certain of these intractable cases acute relapses can be prevented – at a price. The side effects occasioned by these drugs, given orally or by injection, may be pretty intolerable. One percipient and articulate schizophrenic reflected, 'I think that the richness of my pre-injection days (of Moditen, a long-acting phenothiazine) – even with brief outbursts of madness – is preferable to the numbed cabbage I have become.'[6] Another patient remarked with comparable poignancy: 'Medication obviously plays a part but somehow I prefer to be a little "mad" than overdosed by major tranquillisers.'[7]

It is when faced with such *cris de coeur* that I hear, somewhere in the inner recesses of my mind, the inspired slogan of my Scots colleague – 'Not sedation, but stimulation.' There is a danger, as I see it, that by the injudicious use (or abuse) of psychotropic, or tranquillising drugs – call them what you will – we may be edging back to something akin to the era of bromides and paraldehyde from which we escaped nearly half a century ago.

References

1. Kennedy, A. *Journal of Mental Science*, 1937, **83**, 610.
2. Pullar Strecker, H. *Journal of Mental Science*, 1938, **84**, 146.
3. Kalinowsky, L. B., and Worthing, H. J. *Psychiatric Quarterly*, 1943, **17**, 144.
4. Fleming, G. W. T. H. *Journal of Mental Science*, 1944, **90**, 486.
5. Sargant, W., and Slater, E. *Physical Methods of Treatment in Psychiatry*. London: E. & S. Livingstone Ltd, 1963.
6. Wescott, P. *British Medical Journal*, 1979, **1**, 989.
7. Creer, C., and Wing, J. *Schizophrenia at Home*. Surbiton: National Schizophrenia Fellowship, 1974.

SIX Brain Chemistry and Schizophrenia
by L. L. Iversen

THE IDEA THAT SCHIZOPHRENIA may be associated with a chemical imbalance in the brain is not new; it was already discussed seventy years ago by the psychiatrist Bleuler who gave the first precise description of 'the schizophrenias'. Research on this idea has been given considerable impetus during the last twenty-five years by the discovery that certain drugs can cause hallucinations and other disruptions of normal mental functions somewhat similar to those seen in schizophrenia, whereas other drugs have remarkable beneficial effects in treating some of the cardinal symptoms of the illness. The discovery of drugs which cause hallucinations, such as mescaline and lysergic acid (LSD), prompted a search for possible similar naturally occurring brain chemicals in schizophrenic patients. This search dominated chemical research in this area during the 1950s and 1960s. Although there have been many false leads, this approach has so far proved singularly unsuccessful, and schizophrenia research is littered with the skeletons of biochemical hypotheses which have failed to stand the test of time[1,2]. At the moment more progress is being made through a different approach which seeks to understand the mode of action in the brain of drugs that are known to be of value in treating the symptoms of schizophrenia. It is hoped that understanding how such drugs work may offer useful clues to the biochemical basis of the disease. The fact that drugs can effectively treat some of the symptoms of schizophrenia provides in itself considerable encouragement to further research since it suggests that a modifiable chemical abnormality does exist in the brains of people with the illness.

This chapter will briefly review some of the biochemical ideas that have been proposed in schizophrenia research, and summarise some of the most recent and apparently promising lines of research.

Search for endogenous 'Psychotomimetic' chemicals

There have been numerous attempts to detect abnormal components in the blood or urine of schizophrenic patients, so far with little or no success. Attempting to guess at the chemical nature of such hypothetical 'toxic metabolites', thinking has been dominated by one idea in particular, namely, the so-called 'trans-methylation hypothesis', first proposed by Osmond, Smythies and Harley-Mason in 1952[3]. This is based on the fact that the chemical structure of the hallucinogenic drug, mescaline, bears some resemblance to naturally occurring chemicals, dopamine and noradrenaline, which function as chemical messenger substances in the brain. It was suggested that schizophrenia might be related to overactivity in one of the normal biochemical processes which transfer methyl groups to these amines, leading to an excessive production of toxic methylated derivatives similar in character to mescaline. This hypothesis was later extended to include the possible formation of other methylated hallucinogenic compounds, related to the naturally occurring brain chemical, serotonin.

The methylation hypothesis played a dominant role in biochemical research in schizophrenia in the 1960s. Strong experimental support was apparently given by the finding that the naturally occurring dietary substance, methionine, caused a marked exacerbation of symptoms in many schizophrenic patients. This substance is the natural donor of methyl groups in a number of chemical reactions in the body involving trans-methylation, and it was supposed that methionine might act to increase the formation of the hypothetical hallucinogens in the brain. More recent research, however, has called into question whether the effect of methionine in schizophrenic patients really represents a worsening of pre-existing psychosis, or merely a 'toxic delirium' superimposed on chronic schizophrenia.

Another breakthrough appeared to have been achieved in the early 1960s with reports of the occurrence of a compound in schizophrenic urine which gave a pink spot on paper chromatograms. The so-called 'pink spot' was tentatively identified as 3,4-dimethoxyphenethylamine, a compound which represents a doubly methylated derivative of the naturally occurring brain chemical dopamine, and is closely related chemically to the hallucinogenic drug mescaline. For a while things never looked better for the trans-methylation hypothesis, with the apparent identification of the long sought-after psychotomimetic toxic metabolite. Alas, the outcome of this research was a profusion of pink spots, red faces and continuing confusion. Although some groups appeared to be able to repeat the findings, others were unable to, and the identification of the material as 3,4-dimethoxyphenethylamine proved to be incorrect. This compound, in any case, is not hallucinogenic in man and its presence in small amounts in urine is probably accounted for, not as a product of the metabolism of dopamine in the brain, but from dietary sources, or from the bacterial metabolism of dietary amines in the gut. Other studies have suggested that the 'pink spot' may simply represent a chemical breakdown product of the drug chlorpromazine, widely used in the treatment of schizophrenia.

The trans-methylation hypothesis has survived, nevertheless, in spite of these vicissitudes. The compounds on which the modern version of this hypothesis has focused are methylated derivatives of serotonin, notably N-dimethyltryptamine. This substance is a hallucinogen of the mescaline/LSD type, and can be formed in small amounts in the animal brain. It is also present in small amounts in blood and urine, and a number of reports have suggested that this substance is more commonly found in urine samples from schizophrenic patients than in those from normal controls. Although this line of research seems worth pursuing, the amine is not excreted by all schizophrenic patients. Furthermore, it is also present in the urine of a significant proportion of patients with non-schizophrenic mental illness.

An important weakness of the hypothesis that schizophrenia might be associated with over-production of methylated amines related to the mescaline/LSD family is that the phenomena induced by such drugs differ in important ways from schizophrenia. The major symptoms produced by these hallucinogenic drugs are disorders of perception, with visual rather than auditory hallucinations predominating. In schizophrenia, on the other hand, visual hallucinations are rare and auditory hallucinations much commoner; moreover, schizophrenic patients receiving such drugs report that the drug-induced experience is quite unlike their normal symptoms.

Diet and vitamins

Reports of improvement in schizophrenic patients treated with 'mega-vitamin' or 'orthomolecular therapy' in the form of large doses of nicotinamide or other vitamins have attracted much publicity. However, many careful investigations have indicated that the beneficial effects of nicotinamide in schizophrenia are illusory. Similarly, reports of the importance of other dietary factors in schizophrenia have proved difficult to confirm. One suggestion is that there might be a connection between the intake of cereal products and schizophrenia. Some people are unusually sensitive to a protein known as gluten present in wheat and other cereals which can cause bowel irritation. The possible connection with schizophrenia has been suggested by the apparently higher incidence of schizophrenia in those countries where wheat and cereal products constitute a major part of the diet, and on the reportedly beneficial effects of maintaining schizophrenic patients on a gluten-free diet.

The latest fashions — kidney dialysis and endorphins in schizophrenia

The recent discovery that the brain contains naturally occurring chemicals, the endorphins, which possess many of the properties of morphine and related drugs has generated considerable scientific excitement. The endorphins are small peptides manufactured and utilised normally in the brain, probably as chemical messengers between nerve cells. They appear to play an important role in the brain's ability to modify the input of pain information, and may also play a key role in the pleasure and reward systems of the brain. As has been the case with other developments in our knowledge of brain chemistry, several attempts have already been made to implicate this new family of brain chemicals in schizophrenia. Although morphine itself does not appear to have any beneficial effects in treating the symptoms of schizophrenic illness, a number of extravagant claims have been made recently for the beneficial effects of administering naturally occurring endorphins to schizophrenic patients. In direct contradiction, however, other studies have claimed beneficial effects with the drug naloxone, which acts as a powerful *antagonist* of the effects of morphine and endorphins in the brain. Another, as yet poorly documented suggestion, attempts to link the alleged beneficial effects of treatment by kidney dialysis machines in schizophrenia with the endorphin field. It has been suggested that some schizophrenic patients show considerable improvement by regular treatment on kidney dialysis machines. It is alleged that such treatment may remove a 'toxic metabolite' from the blood, and furthermore that this metabolite may represent an abnormal chemical product derived from endorphin in the brain. Few biochemists take this idea seriously, and it remains to be shown whether or not renal dialysis does indeed have a beneficial effect in schizophrenic patients, or whether the apparent benefits are, as so often in the past with new forms of treatment, unreliable and unrepeatable.

Brain dopamine

In the past decade a new approach to schizophrenia research has emerged, which is based, not on the search for a hypothetical 'toxic metabolite', but on clues obtained from our improved knowledge of the treatment of schizophrenic illness by drugs – the major tranquillisers. In particular, various lines of research have converged to point to the critical role played by the chemical messenger substance, dopamine, in the schizophrenia syndrome. One line of research concerns the effect of the stimulant and appetite-suppressing drug, amphetamine and related drugs, which can induce a schizophrenia-like syndrome in normal people and can exacerbate schizophrenic psychosis. Another experimental approach has emerged from studies of the mode of action of the major tranquillisers used in the treatment of schizophrenia. In both cases, the drugs appear to act on brain dopamine mechanisms. From this has emerged the 'dopamine hypothesis', which proposes that schizophrenia may be associated with an excessive function of dopamine in the brain[2,4].

The existence of dopamine as a chemical transmitter, responsible for carrying messages between nerve cells in the brain, has been known for the past twenty years. The nerve cells which contain dopamine have been precisely mapped in animal and human brains, and are known to be present in a limited number of neuronal circuits. These are particularly abundant in a region of the brain known as the 'basal ganglia' which is important in the control of voluntary movements. A loss of dopamine cells from this area of the brain underlies the symptoms of Parkinson's disease which is characterised by rigidity of the limbs, tremor and an inability to undertake voluntary movements. Dopamine-containing nerve cells, however, are also present in other regions of the brain, notably in those areas involved in emotional behaviour.

Amphetamine effects

The toxic effects of amphetamine in drug addicts are now recognised as one of the most accurate drug-induced models of schizophrenia in man. Whereas the hallucinations induced by mescaline and LSD are readily distinguished from the symptoms of schizophrenia, 'amphetamine psychosis' is clinically indistinguishable from acute or chronic paranoid schizophrenia. Numerous patients with amphetamine psychosis have been misdiagnosed as paranoid schizophrenics. The similarity, indeed, also extends to drug treatment, since drugs such as chlorpromazine and other phenothiazines which are used in the treatment of schizophrenia are also uniquely effective antidotes for amphetamine-induced psychosis. Amphetamine psychosis can reliably be induced in volunteers who receive repeated large doses of the drug, and in such subjects psychosis occurs consistently within 1–4 days after the start of the administration of amphetamine.

Animal studies show clearly that the actions of amphetamines in stimulating behaviour are related to their ability to cause a release of dopamine in the brain. The stimulant effects of amphetamine on animal behaviour are completely abolished if animals are pretreated with compounds that inhibit the synthesis of brain dopamine or which destroy dopamine-containing nerve cells.

Anti-schizophrenic drugs and brain dopamine

The effects of amphetamine in animals or in human addicts and volunteers are reliably blocked by all of the known major tranquillisers used in treating the symptoms of schizophrenia. This is one of the discoveries that have led to the now widely accepted hypothesis that such drugs owe their antipsychotic effects to their ability to block the actions of dopamine in the brain. Chlorpromazine was the first drug of this type to be used effectively in treating schizophrenia, and it has been followed by the introduction of numerous drugs with similar effects. Direct tests of the hypothesis that such drugs act as dopamine antagonists have become possible in recent years with the development of biochemical techniques that allow drug effects on dopamine receptors in brain tissue to be examined in test-tube systems in the laboratory. One such approach involves the use of radioactively labelled tranquilliser drugs, such as haloperidol. These drugs bind sufficiently tightly and specifically to dopamine receptors in brain membranes in minced animal brain tissue to allow their binding to the receptors to be experimentally measured. The effects of other tranquilliser drugs on such receptors can then be assessed by their ability to displace radioactive haloperidol from its receptor binding sites in a test-tube assay. The results obtained indicate an impressive correlation between the activity of tranquilliser drugs in this test system and their clinical activities as measured by the dose needed to control schizophrenic symptoms.

Such findings strongly support the conclusion that the antipsychotic properties of these drugs can be attributed to their dopamine-blocking properties. This in turn suggests further questions. Which of the dopamine systems in the brain is crucial for the antipsychotic effect? Does the mode of action of anti-schizophrenic drugs as dopamine antagonists tell us anything about the biochemical nature of the disease?

The dopamine hypothesis of schizophrenia

The 'dopamine hypothesis' seems to be firmly established in the sense that anti-schizophrenic drugs appear to act by virtue of their dopamine blocking effects in brain. However, whether these findings can be taken to imply that schizophrenia itself may represent a disorder in which there is excessive activity or perhaps an unusually high responsiveness to dopamine in the brain is still not clear. Recent biochemical results obtained by the chemical analysis of brain samples obtained after death from schizophrenic patients appear to support such an idea. Results obtained by Dr. E. Bird and E. Spokes in Cambridge, and by Dr. T. Crow and his colleagues in London have shown that abnormally high amounts of dopamine are present in certain areas of the brain in schizophrenia[5,6]. In addition, biochemical measurements of drug-binding in schizophrenic brain tissue have shown that abnormally high numbers of dopamine receptors are present in most regions of the brain in dying patients with schizophrenia.[5,6]. Both of these findings are consistent with the simplest form of the dopamine hypothesis, suggesting that there may be both abnormally high quantities of dopamine and an unusual responsiveness of brain tissue to dopamine in schizophrenia. The chemical abnormalities appear to be specific to the dopamine systems in the brain, since no biochemical abnormalities could be detected in various other chemical transmitter systems by chemical analyses of the same brain tissues. On the other hand, a major difficulty in interpreting the biochemical findings obtained from the human brain is that the abnormalities in brain dopamine mechanisms that are observed might not be peculiar to the illness itself but merely a consequence of long-term treatment with major tranquilliser drugs which are known to interact with the dopamine mechanisms in the brain. This question can only be resolved by further studies of human brain tissue, including those obtained after death from patients who had not received drug treatment for at least some time before death. Animal studies are also needed to determine the effects on brain chemistry of long-term treatment with anti-schizophrenic drugs.

Prospects for drug development

Whether or not the dopamine-blocking actions of anti-schizophrenic drugs help to explain the nature of the chemical imbalance underlying schizophrenic symptoms, the discovery in itself should prove useful in the development of new and improved anti-schizophrenic drugs. By combining additional pharmacological activities with the dopamine-blocking effect it may be possible to avoid some of the undesirable side-effects caused by many of the existing drugs, including their tendency to symptoms akin to Parkinson's disease and their tendency to cause drowsiness. New preparations of existing powerful drugs such as fluphenazine (Modecate) and flupenthixol (Depixol) as long-lasting depot injections have already had an important impact on drug treatment in schizophrenia. Such injections allow slowly-absorbed drugs to be administered at intervals as long as one month. The introduction of new drugs taken by mouth with long-lasting actions is a likely development. The development of new drugs with more selective actions on dopamine receptors in particular brain regions may also be possible, since current research suggests that several categories of dopamine receptors may exist in varying proportions in different regions of the brain.

There has not yet been any definite identification of a biochemical abnormality in schizophrenia. Nevertheless, considerable progress has been made in understanding the beneficial effects of drug treatment in terms of brain chemistry. It is perhaps worth considering whether the quest for a metabolic defect in schizophrenia is meaningful, and how it might improve our understanding of the disease if one were to be discovered. The ability of drugs to have profound effects on the symptoms of schizophrenic illness strongly suggests that the search for a biochemical disorder or imbalance is meaningful, and that biochemical abnormalities must underly the actual schizophrenic symptoms, whether or not schizophrenia is a single disease entity or a collection of different sub-groups. The identification of a specific biochemical disturbance might help to explain the nature of the brain malfunction underlying such symptoms, although we would still not understand how this biochemical abnormality came about. Why is it that twins with identical genetic composition show on average only a 50% concordance for the disease? What are the mechanisms by which environmental and social factors interact with genetic predisposition to cause schizophrenia, or to lead to a relapse in those successfully treated? It would certainly be naive to suppose that the discovery of a metabolic defect could be regarded as 'the cause' of schizophrenia. Nevertheless, neurochemical research seems likely to be a promising way to unravel at least some of these complexities.

References

1. Kety, S. S. *New England J. Med.*, *276*, 325, 1967.
2. Iversen, L. L. In *Schizophrenia. Towards a New Synthesis*, Ed. J. Wing, p. 89. London, Academic Press, 1978.
3. Osmond, H., Smythies, J. R. and Harley-Mason, J. *J. ment. Sci.*, *98*, 309, 1952.
4. Crow, T. J., Deakin, J. F. W., Johnston, E. C., and Longden, A. *Lancet*, *2*, 563, 1976.
5. Owen, F., Crow, T. J., Poulter, M., Cross, A. J., Longden, A. and Riley, G. J. *Lancet*, *2*, 223, 1978.
6. Bird, E. D., Spokes, E. G. and Iversen, L. L. *Brain*, 1979.
7. Seeman, P., Lee, T., Chau-Wong, M. and Wong, K. *Nature*, *261*, 717, 1976.

SEVEN Rehabilitation
by Dr. Roger Morgan

REHABILITATION will here mean a joint venture undertaken
by disabled people and their helpers, designed to improve the
disabled person's competence. Disability is always multiple
(mental, social, occupational, sometimes physical etc.) and each
element may vary in degree from mild to crippling, so that in any
group of rehabilitees there tends to be a very wide range of total
disability. Schizophrenia is the commonest cause of chronic
mental disability, so that services tend to be designed with the
needs of chronic schizophrenics in mind.

It is a cliché that rehabilitation should begin on the day of
admission to hospital, and that rehabilitation and treatment
should thereafter proceed hand in hand. In one sense this is
perhaps as true for schizophrenia as it is for any other mental or
physical disability. But in another sense it can be very
misleading. Active rehabilitation of a schizophrenic cannot really
begin unless and until treatment with appropriate drugs, if
necessary, has restored him to a certain level of stability and
responsibility – without which he is simply unable to supply the
required cooperation in the joint venture.

The most important single ingredient in schizophrenic
rehabilitation is stimulation, but it needs to be carefully judged in
amount and deliberately neutral in its emotional tone. If the
amount is excessive, or the emotional involvement becomes too
strong, the schizophrenic responds by breaking down; whenever
that happens all stimulation has to be withheld for the time being
and as a result rehabilitation comes to a temporary halt. On the
other hand, if too little stimulation is routinely given, the
schizophrenic is prone to withdraw further.

The attitudes of relatives, staff and other helpers (collectively
called staff for short) are therefore very important. Conventional
overprotection is disastrous. Staff do well to see their role as
helping patients to help themselves. Individual patients respond

better to certain helpers than others and to certain techniques than others; and all concerned can profitably learn by experience who and what is best in individual cases. If possible it is best to indicate kindly and consistently to a patient that one's expectations of him are high as opposed to low — but not, of course, to the extent of expecting the impossibly high.

Tactically, it should be the staff aim to set the scene to enable a patient to achieve a mini-success in any department of life. One hopes that he will enjoy this unusual experience and will want to try to repeat it in the same and other departments of life too. If repeated attempts to fan a flicker of motivation into a flame in this way do not succeed the outlook is poor, because the joint venture will fail if either staff or patient motivation is persistently lacking.

There are three definable groups of patients who lack indispensable assets and in our present state of comparative ignorance therefore carry a poor prognosis. Firstly, there are some pathetic young schizophrenics, still in the early years of their illness, who for some unknown reason do not respond to conscientious anti-psychotic drug treatment and remain unable and unwilling to cooperate responsibly. Secondly, there are people with anti-social tendencies who prove to be more than a rehabilitation service can cope with. And thirdly, there are people whose schizophrenic attack is so severe that they are left so fragmented and devastated by it that they lack the necessary residual assets for their helpers to build upon. Many years of illness, or many years in hospital, do not by themselves necessarily imply a hopeless prognosis. Outcome is governed not by history so much as by the degree of the residual disability, because each individual's scope for improvement from this is limited rather than unlimited — and miracles seldom happen.

Without active and enthusiastic medical leadership it is unusual to find a rehabilitation programme even being set up let alone surviving and thriving in the face of inevitable frustrations and disappointments. Unfortunately, few doctors care for chronic illness so that training in its management is neglected. Low prestige is attached to psychiatric rehabilitation and so far Government policy has failed to implement a repeated recommendation that one consultant should be put in medical charge of a District's rehabilitation service. However, there is a recent welcome trend by several hospitals to take the initiative and appoint such consultants.

A rehabilitation service should be designed so that a rehabilitee can progress through it, and ideally beyond it, by a series of small steps. To take as an example: work re-training jobs initially need to be simple and plentifully supervised and working hours have to be short. The most severely disabled people cannot go beyond this. The less disabled will also fail if suddenly confronted with much more difficult conditions, but will find it possible to progress if jobs gradually get more complicated, hours get progressively longer, and supervision is imperceptibly withdrawn.

The constant aim of the staff task is to prepare the patient to meet the demands of the more difficult conditions that lie ahead. If a way can be found to do this effectively then morale and confidence are built up and dignity is preserved. At some stage during the process the rehabilitee who started in hospital is discharged. This episode is called resettlement, a special term needed to distinguish it clearly from the long ongoing process of rehabilitation. Too often, alas, rehabilitation ends when resettlement occurs. But what is even worse is to provide no rehabilitative preparation before resettlement and to imagine that rehabilitation begins with resettlement.

In principle, the best way to prepare a hospital rehabilitee for his eventual resettlement is to make life in hospital as much like life outside as possible. In this way hospital life may be expected to make patients progressively more fit to contend with conditions they will have to face in the future. As a corrective to the anti-therapeutic state to which the worst of institutions are too prone to sink, six criteria are suggested.

The weekly programme of activities should be sufficiently varied to enable patients to distinguish one day from another and preserve their orientation in time.

Each working day should be divided into a working part and a leisure part, with the expectation that all patients will do some work rather than some patients will do all the work.

Rates of payment for work done should be determined objectively as a result of negotiations outside the institution and eschew fallible staff judgements, which can in themselves be a potent way of clinging to total-institution status.

Patients should not eat, sleep, work and play in the same place. Within reason, the more different the places available for an individual patient to do these things, the better.

Within the valuable supportive framework of institution-life, patients need to keep alive their ability to make their personal decisions and exercise their personal choice as, for example, in clothes, diet, occupation and leisure. Staff attitudes and administrative arrangements should actively encourage rather than covertly frustrate and prevent such opportunities.

Each patient needs to have a small definable part of the institution which for the time being is his own territory by right. This usually consists of the patient's bed area, which if well designed and well equipped, provides valuable privacy.

The nearer one can get to observing these six criteria, the smaller the risk of causing any institutional damage and, indeed, the better the prospect of repairing any previous damage. Given observance of these criteria there need, therefore, be no feeling of reluctance to keep a patient in hospital in cases where this appears to be the treatment of choice.

Work is an essential element of any good rehabilitation enterprise. It has direct and indirect value. It is relevant, of course, to the improvement of occupational disability, but people often forget that the work situation is also full of social ingredients and, therefore, of valuable opportunities for social rehabilitation. The value of a given work programme therefore depends very much on the interpersonal and material conditions under which it is purveyed and the extent to which these exploit work's healing properties. Ideally, a wide range of different jobs should be available in order to satisfy different tastes, talents and needs. Work should, if possible, be plentiful, attractive and fairly paid, in order to meet motivational and vocational needs. Simple repetitive work provides a good teaching-learning situation for retraining in basic work skills. Hospital departments (under careful clinical supervision) can provide valuable further training in service-type jobs. Some white-collar work needs to be available, but is more difficult to provide, and few places, if any, have solved the problem of rehabilitating the schizophrenic with a residual high intelligence. A hierarchy of work situations is the ideal, and conditions in the top grade of work should differ as little as possible from conditions of work in open employment, including, of course, the length of the working day.

The need for anti-psychotic drug treatment is not reduced, but, if anything, increased by rehabilitation which is quite deliberately a more stimulating and stressful process than custodial care. One compensation is that the improved opportunities for patient-assessment and staff-observation and staff-communication, implicit in any good rehabilitation regime, greatly enhance the information available to the physician and so enable him to monitor effectively the effects of the drugs he prescribes. For each individual patient a search is desirable for the particular drug and dose which suits him best. The minimum required dose (which in a small number of cases means no drugs) is the best one. Side-effects must be avoided if possible, and one is then reduced to reaching, in individual cases, a compromise between the optimum anti-psychotic effect and the mimimum of unavoidable side-effects. Patient cooperation is vital, and to this end the search for appropriate treatment ideally should be a joint venture between doctor and patient leading, as a result of sympathetic discussion, to a feeling of trust in the doctor by the patient. Heavy case loads make this difficult to attain. Drug treatment, faithfully continued, under medical supervision (in the face of all the temptations to abandon it), is in most cases an essential ingredient of efficient after-care.

Assessment and repeated reassessment, leading to formulation and updating of individual treatment programmes, are a prominent feature of good rehabilitation practice. Representatives of different disciplines contribute to these programmes. The need to coordinate their individual contributions and activities requires some sort of comprehensive system of clinical conferences to include all patients under care.

Basic social skills are impaired in many patients and need to be re-taught as, for example, in personal hygiene, personal appearance, care of clothes, writing letters, saving money, shopping and in travelling. With few exceptions it is a waste of time trying to teach schizophrenic patients anything more elaborate or abstract or emotionally-loaded than this.

For selected patients in need of more advanced domestic training, the model kitchen, the mock flat and the halfway hostel can provide valuable preparation for life in lodgings in a hostel or in a group home.

Community nurses have proved of great value as a means of ensuring continuity of experienced after-care under medical direction and supervision in difficult cases.

Adequate time is the final essential ingredient if rehabilitation is to be done thoroughly. People fail to recognise that rehabilitation is such a long and slow process. It takes months or years rather than days or weeks. Indeed, it may be said that if the chronic disability lasts for the rest of the person's lifetime, then so, in a sense, does his need for rehabilitation. The recent change in the style of treatment from hospital care to (inadequate) community care, has done nothing to reduce the degree, or the duration, of the disability inflicted by chronic schizophrenia. What it has done is to conceal from all but the relatives the extent to which the desperate need for skilled care in special environments, as described throughout this paper, are unmet. Delivery of this care is being reduced progressively in step with the reduction in the number of available beds and in tune with the prevailing professional, (but unfounded) fear that prolonged hospital care inevitably harms people.

It is hoped that the pendulum of fashion swings back again before too long – before too much suffering has been inflicted on ex-patients and their families, before scarce rehabilitation skills and environments have atrophied and disappeared, and before the community (which doesn't care unless personally involved) revolts as the result of having a steadily increasing number of disabled people at large without adequate arrangements for their care. Greater professional awareness of, and interest in, chronic illness coupled with appropriate political action would ideally produce more available beds. These are indispensable if the process of rehabilitation is to be given back the time that it needs. Three particular patient-needs repay generous investment of time. They are firstly, the individual search for mental stability through the most effective drug and dose; secondly, the reshaping by the disabled person (with skilled help) of his own faulty attitudes; and thirdly, the whole process of social and occupational retraining.

EIGHT The Law in Relation to Mental Disorder
by Dr. Henry R. Rollin

IN THE FEARS and phantasies of the lay public, mental illness, including of course schizophrenia, is associated with disturbed, bizarre or dangerous behaviour. This is unfortunately true in a small proportion of cases, but it is safe to say that the majority of the mentally ill lead their lives without posing a threat to the safety or susceptibilities of their families or the public at large. But if treatment is required, either inpatient or outpatient, how is this to be obtained?

The implementation of the humane Mental Health Act 1959 was an extremely important milestone in the sad history of the way that the mentally disordered, including the mentally ill, have been dealt with. One of the principal articles of faith on which the Act is built, indeed, is that wherever possible the mentally disordered should be treated on an informal, that is, voluntary basis. In this respect the Act has been eminently successful. Virtually 100% of psychiatric outpatients are treated informally as are approximately 90% of inpatients. It is worth remembering in this context that prior to the Mental Treatment Act 1930, generally speaking, no patient could receive treatment in a mental hospital unless he had been 'certified', a procedure which carried with it a lifelong stigma.

Even so, there is still a minority of patients whose liberty must be taken away for varying periods. This is a most serious matter and is always undertaken as a measure of last resort in the interests of the patient's health or safety, or for the protection of others. If, then, compulsory admission is seen to be imperative, it is effected under Part IV of the Act (Compulsory Admission to Hospital and Guardianship). Where, however, the mentally ill person has committed an offence against the criminal law the Court may see fit to admit him compulsorily to hospital under Part V of the Act (Admission of Patients concerned in Criminal Proceedings); or the Court may deem it appropriate to place the offender on probation under the Powers of Criminal Courts Act 1973. In certain circumstances a person may be removed by the police 'to a place of safety', usually a hospital, under Section 136 of the Act without any offence being alleged.

We may now consider the methods of compulsory admission to hospital separately and in some detail.

Compulsory Admission Under Part IV, Mental Health Act 1959

The Sections of this part of the Act usually employed are 25, 29 and 26, each having a somewhat different function.

In all cases there has to be an application for admission to hospital which must be founded on medical recommendations. The application is made either by the mental welfare officer (the successor to the 'duly authorised officer') or by the nearest relative, except in Section 29 when any relative can make the application.

The nearest relative in rank order is: (a) husband or wife, (b) son or daughter, (c) father, (d) mother, (e) brother or sister, (f) grandparent, (g) grandchild, (h) uncle or aunt, (i) nephew or niece.

Two medical recommendations are required, except in Section 29, when only one is required. One recommendation is normally made by the patient's usual general practitioner and the other by a medical practitioner approved under Section 28 of the Act, as having special experience in the diagnosis or treatment of mental disorder.

It is noteworthy that applications in all cases are made technically to the managers of the hospital to which admission is sought. Since the reorganisation of the National Health Service the managers of hospitals are the Area Health Authorities. It is most often the responsible Medical Officer, usually a consultant psychiatrist under whose care the patient is admitted, who has formally to agree to accept the application.

Section 25 is used for the admission of a patient for observation for a period of not more than 28 days. During this period the patient may be discharged by the responsible Medical Officer or the hospital managers. The nearest relative does not have the right to order discharge.

At the expiration of the period of observation the patient must be discharged, or if this is undesirable on clinical grounds the procedure under Section 26 can be implemented. If, on the other hand, there is need for further treatment and the patient is willing to remain in hospital he may do so as an informal patient.

Section 29 is used for the admission of a patient in any case of *urgent necessity* and is valid for a period of 72 hours only. At the expiry of this period the patient must be discharged. If, however, it is essential on clinical grounds for him to be detained for further treatment this, if possible, should be on an informal basis. If this is not possible, subject to a second medical recommendation becoming available, the period of compulsory care is extended to 28 days in accordance with Section 25.

Section 26 is used for the admission of a patient for *treatment* and is valid for one year in the first instance. Application may be made by the mental welfare officer or the nearest relative, but the former cannot proceed if the latter objects. If the objection is considered to be unreasonable, the mental welfare officer may apply to a County Court for an Order. A patient admitted under Section 26 may be discharged by the responsible Medical Officer, the managers of the hospital, or by the nearest relative. The responsible Medical Officer can oppose the discharge by the relative on the grounds that the patient, if discharged, would be likely to act in a manner dangerous to others or to himself or if it is necessary in the interests of the patient's health for him to be detained (S43[3]). If this happens the relative may apply within 28 days to a Mental Health Review Tribunal in respect of the patient. Further applications to the Tribunal may be made yearly.

The patient himself may apply to a Mental Health Review Tribunal within six months of the day of his admission, but he may not make another application during the twelve months beginning with the date of his admission. Thereafter he may make an application annually.

Compulsory Admission under Part V, Mental Health Act 1959

A further important principal enshrined in the Mental Health Act is that if a person suffering from mental disorder commits a criminal offence he should receive treatment and not punishment. Part V of the Act is concerned with the disposal of the mentally abnormal offender, although a proportion become the subject of a probation order.

It is important at this juncture to point out that offenders against the criminal law do not fall neatly into two categories, the sane and the insane. There is no good reason why the same individual cannot be insane and a criminal, or to put it more succinctly, both mad and bad. This duality is made abundantly clear if the case histories of some mentally abnormal offenders are studied. They show clearly that the same individual may for many years be lobbed like a tennis ball over the net that separates the mental hospital system and the prison system. Eventually it becomes evident that neither system is effective; he is, in effect, incurable in terms of one, and incorrigible in terms of the other. It is also as well to point out that a high proportion of such unfortunates are rootless schizophrenics for whom inadequate provision is made in the community. The problems created by this stage-army of mentally abnormal offenders have been aggravated by the policy of 'discharge and be damned' adopted by so many of our mental hospitals, and a parallel policy of refusing to admit 'chronics' via the Courts on the grounds that they are incurable. It has been forgotten, seemingly, that one of the functions of a mental hospital is, or should be, to offer asylum, in the best sense of that much abused word.

The crimes committed by the mentally abnormal offenders, crimes attributable to their disorder that is, form only a small fraction of the totality of crime. For the most part their crimes are relatively petty and may, as with the type of vagrant schizophrenic described above, be committed in order to live. Common examples are stealing milk from doorsteps or fruit from street markets. It must be conceded, however, that a tiny minority of crimes, committed for the most part by the paranoid variety of schizophrenic, are infinitely more serious and may include deliberate, cold-blooded murder. Sometimes in the crimes committed there is a bizarre, or ghoulish element which gives a clue to the nature of the mental disorder of the offender.

Once the offender has been arrested by a police officer and a decision taken to prosecute (in certain circumstances the decision is not to prosecute and the procedure here is described later in this chapter) the due process of law continues. If there is then reason to believe that the accused is suffering from mental disorder the customary practice is to remand him in custody for psychiatric examination.

When the medical reports confirming the presence of mental disorder are available the Court is empowered to dispose of the accused in a variety of ways. The most important are:

Hospital Order (Section 60)

If the accused is proved to have committed the offence the Court may make a Hospital Order if it is satisfied:

On the evidence of two doctors, at least one of whom is approved under Section 28 of the Act, that the offender is suffering from one of the categories of mental disorder, i.e. mental illness, severe subnormality, subnormality, or psychopathic disorder, of a nature or degree which warrants his detention in hospital for medical treatment.

That a particular hospital is willing to admit the patient within 28 days.

That in the circumstances of the case, the making of a Hospital Order is the most suitable method of disposing of the case.

A lower Court, however, is not obliged to proceed to a conviction if the medical evidence substantiates a diagnosis of mental illness or of severe subnormality.

There are limitations to the use of this section. It cannot be used, for example, where the sentence is fixed by law, which for practical purposes means murder: nor can it be used for petty offences which are not punishable with imprisonment. It can, however, be used in cases of infanticide or manslaughter, including murder reduced to manslaughter as a result of a successful defence of diminished responsibility.

Generally speaking a Hospital Order has the same effect as an Order made under Section 26, a treatment order with the exception that the nearest relative does not have the power to discharge, although he is given the right to apply to a Mental Health Review Tribunal once a year. The patient himself may apply to that Tribunal in the same way as a patient admitted under Section 26.

Restriction Orders (Section 65)

This Section empowers superior Courts, but not Magistrates'

Courts, to superimpose on a Section 60 Order a 'restriction order' for a specified period, or 'without limitation of time'. Such an Order is made if the Court considers this necessary for the protection of the public, taking into account the nature of the offence, the antecedents of the offender, and the risk of committing further offences if set at large.

A patient under a Restriction Order is under the direct control of the Home Secretary and may not be discharged, transferred or granted leave of absence without his consent. Neither the patient nor his nearest relative may apply to a Mental Health Review Tribunal, but the Home Secretary may refer the patient's case to a Tribunal for advice at any time. Furthermore, the patient may request him to do so after a year, two years and each subsequent two year period.

Probation Orders
The original Probation of Offenders Act, 1907, enabled a Court to refrain from punishing a mentally disordered offender even if he had not used his disorder as a defence. The same enablement is today vested in the Criminal Courts Act, 1973 (Section 3). The objective in making such an order is that the probationer should submit to treatment 'with a view to improving his mental condition'.

The limitations in making an order are:

Evidence must be given by a medical practitioner recognised under Section 28 of the Mental Health Act, 1959.

The evidence must be to the effect that the mental condition while it 'required and was susceptible to treatment' was not such as to justify compulsory methods. A probation order seems intended for use in mild disorders.

The Court must be satisfied that satisfactory arrangements have been made for treatment to be given, either on an inpatient or outpatient basis.

Treatment must be carried out by or under a duly qualified medical practitioner.

The probationer must consent to treatment, but this would not oblige him to consent to any treatment, for example, Electroconvulsive Treatment or Psychosurgery, if the Court felt that his refusal 'in all the circumstances' was reasonable.

The Order must specify the length of treatment which can be

for a full three years, the statutory limit of a Probation Order.

As with a Section 60 Order a Probation Order cannot be used for offences carrying a fixed sentence, for example, murder, but unlike Section 60 it can be used for non-imprisonable offences such as drunkenness.

The subject of a Probation Order is in a somewhat anomalous position: as far as the mental hospital or outpatient clinic are concerned the probationer is an informal patient, but from a legal standpoint he is liable to sanctions if he breaks off treatment unreasonably or absconds. Technically, he could be brought before the Court and could be given some other form of punishment, even imprisonment.

Section 136 'Place of Safety'

In this Section of the Mental Health Act, 1959, there is no question of prosecution. The Act states that, 'if a constable finds in a place to which the public have access a person who appears to him to be suffering from mental disorder and to be in immediate need of care and control, the constable may, if he thinks it necessary to do so in the interests of that person or for the protection of other persons remove that person to a place of safety ...'. In practice a place of safety is almost invariably a psychiatric facility.

A patient admitted to hospital under Section 136 may be detained for a period not exceeding 72 hours so allowing time for him to be examined by a medical practitioner, or if need by, by a mental welfare officer. At the end of the 72 hours the patient must be discharged unless steps have been taken under Part IV of the Act to detain him further should his clinical condition merit such a step. Alternatively, he may remain in hospital on an informal basis if he expresses a wish to do so.

There is positive proof that Section 136 is being increasingly used, particularly in the Metropolis. What is particularly important is that there is evidence relating to its use as a means of resolving social crises involving individuals – in a high proportion of cases chronic schizophrenics – who have only recently been discharged from mental hospitals and for whom inadequate provision has been made for their care in the community.

A few illustrations of the way in which Section 136 is used

might be instructive. The accounts to be given are taken verbatim from the police reports accompanying the patients, all of them chronic schizophrenics, to hospital.

Case 1. 'Had delusions that he was the Messiah and, as he did not get recognition, removed his clothes and walked down Charing Cross Road'.

Case 2. 'Breaking wing-mirrors and aerials of stationary vehicles and hurling them at passing motor cars and nearby private houses'.

Case 3. 'Violent and confused and masturbating in the street'.

Case 4. 'Trying to expose himself to girls waiting at the bus stop. Was vague and mute'.

It will be noted that although the behaviour is not in itself particularly dangerous it is embarrassing to the public and there can be little doubt that the removal of the people concerned to a 'place of safety' was fully justified.

Although the emphasis in this chapter has been on the methods whereby the mentally disordered can be compulsorily admitted to a psychiatric facility, care has been taken to show that, built into the system, are the means to prevent the abuse of these powers.

In this context, it must be stressed that the periods during which patients may by compulsorily detained in hospital under the various Sections of the Act are maxima. There is no reason why the responsible medical officer cannot discharge a patient at any time during the period of detention should his clinical condition warrant it. The exception is, of course, a patient detained under Sections 60/65, a Restriction Order, where discharge lies in the hands of the Home Secretary. Furthermore, as has already been pointed out, the managers of the hospital or in appropriate cases the nearest relative, may order the discharge of the patient.

But the most important innovation by far in the Mental Health Act, 1959, are the Mental Health Review Tribunals. These Tribunals are independent bodies who may, after hearing the application, direct the patient's discharge and must do so if, for example, they are satisfied that he is no longer suffering from any of the categories of mental disorder, or that it is not necessary in the interests of his health and safety, or for the protection of others, that he should continue to be detained.

Finally, care was taken previously to underline the fact that although patients under Sections 60/65 Restriction Orders cannot apply directly to the Tribunal they have the right to request the Home Secretary to refer their case to a Tribunal. It is for the Home Secretary, of course, to accept or reject the advice given.

NINE The Right to Care – The Plight of the Chronic Schizophrenic in the Community *by Dr. Henry R. Rollin*

THE MENTALLY ILL, like the poor, have always been with us. Indeed, as examples of society's underprivileged the two groups are in some ways analogous. Both groups lack political muscle and as a result tend to be relegated to the back of the queue when the fiscal cake is being shared out. Crumbs rather than a fair slice is the best they can hope for.

The two groups, however, are by no means mutually exclusive. There are those who suffer from mental illness but are spared pecuniary disadvantages and for them adequate facilities have always been available. If their families were unable to cope, then, for at least the last three hundred years, there have been institutions which, for payment, were prepared to do so. There was, and still is, a well recognised 'trade in lunacy', a trade that was carried out in institutions variously called 'madhouses', 'private licensed houses', or 'private asylums' or 'mental nursing home' to use the euphemism of today. It may be as well to add that, due to ever-rising costs, there is a decreasing number of families sufficiently well-to-do to be able to afford private care.

But our primary concern is with those unfortunates who are doubly disadvantaged in that they are both poor and mentally ill, who at all times have included among their ranks a high proportion of those we now call 'schizophrenics'. Their story is a sad one.

In mediaeval times it is likely that at least a few mentally ill paupers were accommodated in infirmaries. It is known that religious houses must also have played their part. The Priory of St. Mary of Bethlem founded in 1247, later to become Bethlem Hospital, is the best known example. Until the early 18th century it was indeed the only public institution, small as it then was, for the care of the insane. But what must be stressed, in the context of this book, is that in those remote days, particularly in rural areas, 'community care' was a real entity, much more real, alas, than it is today. The family or the village, which was in effect an extended family, looked after their mentally ill and their intellectually retarded as best they could. The village idiot, a collective term for either or both varieties of mental disorder, existed in fact as well as in fiction. However, if the symptoms they presented proved in some way embarrassing to the community it was possible for the afflicted to be 'boarded out' at the expense of the parish in private dwelling houses, or in 'madhouses'. If their symptoms took the form of serious disturbances of behaviour to a degree that the afflicted could be construed as being 'furiously mad and dangerous' they could be locked up 'in such a secure place ... as such justices shall direct and appoint' where, if necessary, they could be chained.

The latter half of the 18th century was remarkable for the humanity with which the approach to this particular social problem was made. This was exemplified by the fact that as a result of public subscription a number of institutions for the care of the insane were founded, such as St. Luke's in London and The Retreat at York.

Unfortunately, the situation deteriorated markedly in the early part of the 19th century, due in the main to the population explosion of the Industrial Revolution, which resulted in the swamping of the existing facilities. The insane, together with other varieties of the mentally disordered, spilled out onto the streets as vagrants and into the workhouses, houses of correction and gaols. The parallel between what happened in those far-off days and what is happening in our own day and age has been made clear in the chapters of this book.

However, the scandalous treatment of the mentally disordered, highlighted by the revelations of grievous abuse and cruelties in the York Lunatic Asylum and at Bethlem, stirred the conscience of the powers-that-be. In 1815 a Parliamentary Select Committee was set up to consider 'of provisions being made for the better regulation of madhouses in England'. It was found that, 'if the treatment of those mentally disordered in the middling or in the lower classes of life shut up in hospitals, private madhouses, or parish workhouses is looked at, your committee are persuaded that a case cannot be found where remedy is more urgent'.

As a result of this most serious indictment an Act amending the 1808 Act was introduced in 1815 which provided for money to be borrowed by the counties for the purpose of building asylums. This Act heralded the beginning of the county asylum movement. But the counties themselves dragged their feet until 1845 when they were no longer exhorted but *compelled* to build asylums. Again, it is in no way difficult to draw a parallel between the lack of enthusiasm shown by the counties in getting on with the job of building asylums and so putting right a social wrong and the local authorities of today who show an equal reluctance to provide the community facilities they were exhorted to provide under the Mental Health Act of 1959. Would, one is entitled to ask, the Government of today be prepared to use compulsion rather than exhortation in order to correct another grievous wrong?

But to return to our brief historical survey. By and large there can be no doubt that, despite certain vicissitudes, there has been a growing enlightenment of the public in England in its attitude to the mentally ill which has been reflected in legislative changes.

The Lunacy Act of 1890 is the basic Act out of which subsequent legislation evolved. In 1930 the Mental Treatment Act was passed. The name itself is of paramount importance in that for the first time it overtly conceded that mental illness was treatable. Of equal importance was the opportunity provided for the voluntary or temporary admission of patients to mental hospitals thus avoiding the stigma of certification with all its social implications. On 5 July, 1948, the National Health Service Act of 1946 came into effect and linked mental and physical illness and thus for the first time ever there appeared on the Statute Book the term 'mental health', in itself a significant step forward.

However, few would doubt that the Mental Health Act, 1959, was potentially the most compassionate instrument of legislation of its kind yet devised in England or, indeed, elsewhere. The intent of the Act is precisely stated in the preamble which reads: 'An Act to repeal the Lunacy and Mental Treatment Acts, 1890 to 1938 and to make fresh provision with respect to the treatment and care of mentally disordered persons and with respect to their property and affairs'.

The Act was the outcome of lengthy and searching

deliberations by the Royal Commission on Mental Health Law (1957) and adopted as official policy by the Government of the day. In acknowledging the need for reform the Commission recognized that: 'advances in medical knowledge, new methods of treatment and the development of new organs of government and new social services have naturally demanded changes in the medical and administrative methods by which these objects are pursued'.

In furthering these objectives the recommendations of the Royal Commission were written into the Act and defined the obligations and functions of the hospital and local authorities. In effect they reversed the long-accepted practice of isolating mental patients in large institutions, themselves often isolated in remote parts of the country. It was hoped to prevent admission to a hospital of any sort by comprehensive out-patient services, but if admission proved inevitable, then this was to be in the first instance to psychiatric departments of general hospitals. The desirability of keeping in-patient treatment to a minimum, and as a corollary, to return the patient as soon as possible to the care of the community, or to 'community care' as it has come to be known, was the principal article of faith. Furthermore, it was emphasized that, 'the division of functions between the hospitals, local authorities and other official bodies should be broadly the same in relation to mentally disordered patients as in relation to others'.

Implicit in these recommendations is the obligation by the community, that is the local authority, to set up prophylactic services and all types of community care for those who do not need or no longer need in-patient care. They would include day or residential training centres, residential accommodation in private homes or hostels, especially for the old, and general social help or advice. Diagnostic clinics were to be established on the lines of child-guidance clinics. At these centres clinical conferences between hospital and local authority staffs on the disposal of individual cases could be held. They would in effect become the local Mental Health headquarters.

Unfortunately – and here's the rub – no date was given as to when the local authorities should meet their obligations as laid down in the Act, and what in effect is to be discussed here is the extent to which the realisation of dreams of a psychiatric utopia remain latent and to what extent they have been fulfilled in the 19 years since the 1959 Act came into operation.

Basically the two essential planks on which the new Act was originally built were the new and allegedly potent methods of psychiatric treatment and the mandatory transfer of emphasis for the care of mental patients from the mental hospitals to the community. A wave of sublime optimism had swept the country at that time, based to no small extent on very favourable statistical forecasts provided by experts. Both the optimism and the forecasts were seized upon by the then Minister of Health, Mr. Enoch Powell, and woven into his Hospital Plan of 1962 in which it was predicted that by 1975 there would be a reduction by nearly half in the number of local mental hospital beds and that their function would be split between community agencies and general hospitals.

How sound have these two planks proved to be? To take the new methods of treatment first: the so-called 'tranquillisers' in particular have undoubtedly produced a revolution in treatment if the sheer tonnage alone of these drugs dispensed through the U.K. and the rest of the world is taken as an index of their popularity. Certainly, in the treatment of schizophrenia, which still remains the overriding problem of mental hospital practice, they do appear to effect a remission earlier than might otherwise be expected. But what they seem incapable of doing with any degree of certainty is to prevent relapses. How else may one explain the alarming number of re-admissions to mental hospitals of patients who all too often have been only recently discharged? The 'open-door' policy of yesterday, it might be said, has in effect been transmuted into the 'revolving-door' policy of today.

The second plank, which calls for the most careful inspection, and has for us a particular relevance, relates to 'community care'. No one would deny the advisability in principle of such a switch of emphasis, but the sad fact remains that before attempting to put this major operation into effect, little was done to determine if indeed the community cared.

In all fairness, it must be stated that in certain localities a real attempt has been made to translate the concept of 'community care' into a working reality. Psychiatric units in general hospitals have been established, day hospitals and hostels, either purpose-built or conversions from existing buildings, have been constructed, and a substantial increase in medical and ancillary workers, i.e. psychiatric social workers, trained and untrained social workers and mental welfare officers, has been realised. But for the country as a whole the field of community care is less green and less lush. Some of it is paved with good intentions, but unfortunately a large part is an arid waste which for lack of money and personnel has failed to be cultivated. For instance, as recently as March 1974 it is officially stated that: '31 local authorities, as then constituted, had no residential accommodation for the mentally ill and 63 no day facilities' (DHSS, 1975).

That there has been a substantial reduction in the number of occupied beds in British mental hospitals cannot be denied. From 1960 to 1970, the number of beds declined by 24,000, and the decline continues. But if our modern methods of treatment are less effective than we had hoped, then the prognosis for the chronic psychotics, particularly the schizophrenics, remains more or less the same. Furthermore, if the concept of community care is for the most part only an inspired slogan, then the socially non-viable, ex-hospital patients must continue to erupt in other ways. Many, as already mentioned, will find their way back to hospital, as is evident in the ever-increasing number of re-admissions which now account for two-thirds of all admissions (DHSS, 1976).[1] Some, less fortunate perhaps, will swell the ranks of the unemployed and unemployable. Others will join the army of vagrants and elbow each other off the park benches, or lengthen the queue outside the doss-houses. Berry & Orwin (1966)[2] report on the steep rise in the number of patients of No Fixed Abode (NFA) admitted to their mental hospital in Birmingham since the 1959 Act came into operation. In their conclusions the authors state *inter alia* : 'Their (the NFA's) plight is evidence that the initial enthusiasm evoked by the new Act for the discharge of chronic psychotics into community care was premature in view of the resources available, and has resulted in the overwhelming of existing community services'. Similarly, Edwards *et al.* (1968)[3] in their study of inmates of Camberwell Reception Centre, London, showed that of a population of 279, 24% had previously been in a mental hospital for reasons other than drinking, and of these

7% had been out of hospital for six months or less. Other studies of 'dossers', e.g. Lodge-Patch (1970)[4] and Scott *et al.* (1966)[5], paint equally gloomy pictures.

There are still further tragic illustrations of the inadequacies of community care. In one report, 'Mental Health of East London in 1966'[6], it was found that of 174 schizophrenics discharged to known addresses from one mental hospital in Epsom, Surrey, only 94 could be traced within 12 months, of whom only 29 were in satisfactory accommodation, 33 were without employment or occupation and 28 were neglecting themselves. The fate of the 80 (nearly 90%) who have disappeared is unknown, but of those who have physically survived there is a strong probability that they will turn up in one of the loci of re-distribution already mentioned.

In all the circumstances, it might be assumed that those ex-patients who have a home to go to are of necessity better off. That this is not so is made quite clear in the reports of the National Schizophrenia Fellowship. In his foreword to the first report (1974), John Pringle[7] castigates those whose duty it was: 'to provide the community support, in replacement for custodial care, which many chronic sufferers (from schizophrenia), unable to fend for themselves, cannot do without'. He goes on: 'The closure of mental hospital wards, which at least provide the basic minimum shelter and life support, goes ruthlessly on, leaving nothing in their place'.

But there is still another locus of redistribution of ex-mental hospital patients not yet mentioned which is considered to be more retrogressive than any other – namely the prisons. There they may land following the commission of offences, usually petty, but not necessarily so by any means. A not inconsiderable proportion of those who, in effect, have exchanged a hospital bed for a prison cell are so severely crippled by their mental illness that they are not socially viable without substantial support which, alas, has not been forthcoming. In the absence of this support the crimes of which they are often found guilty, such as thefts of food, are committed in order for them to survive.

The situation which has developed, and continues to develop, prompted the Principal Medical Officer of Brixton Prison, London (1963)[8], to write: 'I have been impressed over the last few years by the number of people received into prison for mental observation and reports to courts who have been in psychiatric hospitals within twelve months of reception. The figures amount to an alarming total of 384 for 1963'. It is noteworthy that the number so remanded in England and Wales doubled from 6,366 in 1961 to 12,530 in 1974[8] and the number of Hospital Orders (Section 60) rose from 838 to 1,034, an increase of 23%. But these figures are taken from official criminal statistics which do not include mentally abnormal offenders who, for one reason or another, were not prosecuted, but were admitted directly to a mental hospital under emergency procedures. Of special importance in this respect is the increase in the use of Section 136 (Part IV of the Act) which permits the police to deal expeditiously with social crises involving the mentally disordered in public places by removing them to a 'place of safety', in practice, almost invariably a mental hospital. For example, in the 12 mental hospitals administered until very recently by the South-West Metropolitan Regional Hospital Board the number rose from 308 (1.9%) of all admissions in 1865 to 709 (4%) of all admissions, a rise of well over 100% (1973[9]).

It was, indeed, the dramatic rise in the admission of mentally abnormal offenders to Horton Hospital, Epsom, both prosecuted and unprosecuted, since the implementation of the 1959 Act which stimulated my interest in the problem of the mentally abnormal offender. One study (Rollin, 1963[10]) analyses all male offenders admitted to Horton in 1961, the first complete year after the 1959 Act became fully operational. A total of 98 were so admitted, a fivefold increase compared with the 19 admitted under existing legislation in 1959, the last year before the new Act was implemented. Seventy-nine (81%) of those admitted were suffering from schizophrenia. In 63 (66%) offenders there was documentary evidence of previous mental illness, in that 41 had had multiple admissions to mental hospitals and 47 had spent an aggregate of more than six months in them. It is a fair assumption, therefore, that a high proportion of the offenders were not only mentally ill at the time of their offence, but had been chronically so for some considerable time before the particular offence was committed. Fifty-three of those admitted had committed their offences within two years of the last recorded discharge from a mental hospital. Four had failed to survive even for a day. Twelve had collided with the law in under a month, and within a year 43 had done so.

A second study (Rollin 1965[11]) analyses 75 male unprosecuted offenders, the majority of whom were under Section 136, admitted to Horton in the years 1961 and 1962. They revealed psychiatric histories very similar to those obtained in the first enquiry. Thus, of 57 who had a recorded history of previous mental illness, 43 had had multiple admissions to mental hospitals and 27 had spent an aggregate of six months in them. Schizophrenia was again overwhelmingly the commonest single diagnosis which was made in 59 (78%) cases. The incapacity of these chronic psychotics to survive in society as measured by the length of the interval from their discharge from mental hospitals (in less than half was Horton the hospital involved) and their collision with the law was, if anything, more marked. Five cases were arrested on the very day of their discharge, 18 in less than a month and 40 within a year of leaving hospital.

To have criticized 'de-institutionalization', or more precisely, the provisions made thus far to convert the myth of community care into a reality would have been considered a very few years ago not only reactionary, but sacrilegious. It comes, therefore, as a surprise, agreeable as it might be to those who did not side with the big battalions, that the Department of Health and Social Security has performed a nimble somersault. This is evidenced in the recent White Paper[12], 'Better Services for the Mentally Ill' (DHSS, 1975), which contains expressions of indignation which might well have come from the pen of those who for years have criticized official practice if not policy. One or two examples suffice: 'The term "open-door hospital" has like "community care" become with time something of a catchphrase'. Or, even more pertinent; 'Those who work in the health and social services fields have to recognize that families and relatives, and indeed the public at large cannot be expected to tolerate under the name of community care the discharge of chronic patients without adequate arrangements being made for after-care and who perhaps spend their days wandering the streets or become an unbearable burden on the lives of their relatives etc'. But the most important statement of all is that of the then Minister of Health and Social Security, Mrs. Barbara Castle, herself. In the foreword she writes: 'What we have to do is get to grips with shifting the emphasis to community care' — as good an example as one could wish for of the futility of closing the stable door 19 years after the horses have left, or perhaps more accurately, were driven out.

And so, the wheel has gone full circle. The plight of the mentally disordered in the community was recognised at the beginning of the 19th century and their right to care acknowledged. Action, appropriate as it then seemed, was taken. We in the last quarter of the 20th century have an identical obligation, an obligation the National Schizophrenia Fellowship is determined to see fulfilled. We care about these unfortunates in our midst who have the right to care.

References

1. Dept. of Health & Social Security 'Psychiatric Hospitals and Units in England. In-patient statistics from the Mental Health Enquiry for the year 1973'. Statistical and Research Report No. 12. London: HMSO, 1976.

2. Berry, C. & Orwin, A. 'No fixed abode. A survey of mental hospital admissions'. *Brit. J. Psychiat. 112*, 1019–1025, 1966.

3. Edwards, G. Williamson, V. Hawker, A. Hensman, C. and Postoyan, S. 'Census of a reception centre'. *Brit. J. Psychiat. 114*, 1031–1039, 1968.

4. Lodge-Patch, I. C. 'A London Survey'. Proceedings of the Royal Society of Medicine, *63*, 437–441, 1970.

5. Scott, R. Gaskell, P. G. & Norrell D. C. 'Patients who reside in common lodging houses'. *Brit. Medical J.* ii, 1561–1564, 1966.

6. 'Mental Health of East London in 1966'. London: Psychiatric Rehabilitation Association, 1968.

7. National Schizophrenia Fellowship. *Living with Schizophrenia*. Surbiton, Surrey: National Schizophrenia Fellowship, 1974.

8. 'Report of the Work of the Prison Dept. for the years 1961 to 1974'. London: HMSO.

9. 'Rootless Wanderers'. *Brit. Medical J.* iii, 1–2, 1973.

10. Rollin, H. R. 'Social and Legal Repercussions of the Mental Health Act, 1959'. *Brit. Medical J.* i, 786–788, 1963.

11. Rollin, H. R. 'Unprosecuted mentally abnormal offenders'. *Brit. Medical J.* i, 831–835, 1965.

12. Dept. of Health & Social Security 'Better Services for the Mentally Ill'. Cmnd 6233. London: HMSO, 1975.

TEN   A Series of Holes – The Work of the National Schizophrenia Fellowship
by Peggy Pyke-Lees

THE CONCEPT OF COMMUNITY CARE, envisaged in Britain by the Mental Health Act of 1959, encouraged psychiatric hospitals to discharge their patients and limit the number of beds they occupied. It was clearly understood that discharged patients were going to be cared for by benevolent Local Authorities who would provide homes and hostels (short-term and long-term, supervised and unsupervised) as well as a range of other facilities including day centres, rehabilitation units and social clubs. A regular income was to be made available under a new system of social security to those patients whose disability prevented them from working, plus a rent allowance to those who were not living at home. Arrangements were to be made by the Department of Employment to provide re-training schemes and jobs.

What in fact happened? The number of beds in psychiatric hospitals was drastically reduced; indeed, it became as hard to get into hospital as, in former days, it was difficult to get out. Even those who were admitted had no guarantee that they would stay there until they were recovered enough for an independent life in the community. For example, a disturbed, hallucinating girl of twenty-four was discharged home one evening without notice because she was too disruptive in the hospital. At home lived her widowed mother with three younger children. Lamentably, such instances are not uncommon in the experience of members of the Fellowship.

It was, of course, the failure of the plans for social treatment and community care that brought the National Schizophrenia Fellowship into being. Lack of community care facilities and lack of communication between services meant, all too frequently, that patients were suddenly discharged from hospital: those who had homes to go to, went to them. All too often there was no prior warning of the return home of their relative. Many families were confronted by day and night with problems they had not expected. In many cases there had been no communication whatever between hospital and relatives who thus found themselves unexpectedly called upon to look after what could prove to be a bewilderingly difficult patient. These relatives were not aware that there were supposed to be services at hand to help them, and many of their attempts to seek help through the family doctor or consultant psychiatrist, or through the social worker or the clerk in the local Social Security Office, met with dismal failure.

In addition to all the other difficulties there was the fear, shame and stigma of having at home a relative who could neither work nor take part in ordinary daily life. The inclination, therefore, to hide the situation from neighbours and friends (and often from members of the family outside the immediate home) was even stronger than the need to get support from those who should have been in a position to help. The stigma is still serious, serious enough to have prevented the dilemma of the care of the chronic schizophrenic in the community from being dragged into the light of day until an historic date in May 1970.

In that month of that year a courageous man, John Pringle, wrote an article which was published in *The Times* in which he described the problems and the agonies experienced by his family during the ten years of his eldest son's illness. He touched on the difficulty that arose between the parents about the appropriate treatment for their son and on the effects that such an illness had on other children in the family. The response elicited by the article led after two years' hard work by Mr. Pringle and his wife, together with a small group of those who had written to him, to the formation of a national voluntary organisation.

The first task of this Schizophrenia Fellowship was to discover what the facts of the situation were and, to this end, a professional survey was undertaken by Professor J. K. Wing and Mrs. C. Creer of the Maudsley Hospital, London, into the needs of relatives of sufferers from schizophrenia. Since a continuing aim was to enable people everywhere to understand the difficulties experienced by those who had had schizophrenia and by the families and friends who were caring for them, a series of publications was started. These included extracts from letters throwing light on the experiences of families deeply concerned about the lack of proper accommodation and employment for their loved ones for whom earlier expectations of an independent life in the community seemed to have vanished. They also showed anxiety for other members of the family. Their lives shattered, they were forced into social isolation by withdrawing from friends and neighbours just because of the stigma and the fears attached to the disease.

As an example of the helplessness of relatives the following case is cited: an eighteen-year-old boy was acutely ill in a mental hospital. His parents had not been told what his illness was, nor how it was proposed to treat it. They had been refused an appointment with the consultant. The mother, in her distress, took a day off work and travelled thirty miles to the hospital where she sat outside the clinic knowing the doctor was there. After she had waited some hours, the doctor came to her and said, 'I understand you have been waiting to see me. There is nothing I can tell you. Your son will never be better than he is now' — and he walked away. With advice from the National Schizophrenia Fellowship, a second consultant opinion was arranged and it is good to report that the boy is now out of hospital and doing well.

Much of the original purpose in publishing information about schizophrenia and its effect on patients and their families was to force on the attention of the Department of Health and Social Security the need for improvement in social provision. Professional workers who joined the Fellowship were in general agreement that the time had come for a reappraisal of the whole situation of provision. This was largely due to two factors.

First, that patients quite clearly continued to be disabled, and liable to relapse, even though they had only spent a brief time in hospital, or, nowadays, perhaps no time at all.

Secondly, the re-discovery that 'community' (that is, non-hospital) care, also has deficiencies, sometimes quite as great as those of hospitals.

Later, there were encouraging indications that the Fellowship's words were being listened to with attention: the Government White Paper, 'Better Services for the Mentally Ill', published in October, 1975, indicated in its provisions that the Fellowship's words had indeed been heard with attention and that their recommendations had had a substantial impact. In addition to all the educational work, it became, and continues to be, the Fellowship's task to put pressure on statutory authorities, nationally and locally, to improve facilities everywhere for the care of schizophrenics.

One publication is worthy of special note. A brief pamphlet simply entitled 'Schizophrenia', was produced in response to members' requests. It emerged that many members learned only years after the onset of the mental illness what the diagnosis was. No one had ever told them what it meant or what the likely outcome was. They frequently became aware of the diagnosis as the result of reading it on a certificate, or by being told by a counter clerk in the Employment Office or the Social Security Office. A basic statement about schizophrenia was therefore produced and was made available to members. In fact, one member sent a copy to the national press where it received a great deal of publicity. There has since been a steady demand for it including many requests from professional workers of all kinds, from family doctors, social workers and, more recently, from magistrates and the police.

That community care for the chronic schizophrenic has to a large extent devolved upon the police and the prison service is not widely known. Patients who have been discharged into the community after a long stay in hospital all too often find themselves in the hands of the police and sometimes eventually in the courts. Probation Officers, incredulous that a schizophrenic had been refused re-admission to a hospital which had been his home for twenty-nine or more years, are wont to telephone the Fellowship for help in finding somewhere for their client to live where the necessary support would be provided. As the Minister of State, Home Office, said in March, 1977, 'It is no part of a civilised policy to put the mentally ill in prison and to make prisons the receptacles of those whom no other agency in society will accept.' But such is the effect of the policy of community care that, as the 'Report of the work of the Prison Department 1976' pointed out:

> Mentally ill people are entering prisons and borstals in increasing numbers and people of previous good personality, whose offences frequently stem solely from their illness, are now being refused admission to psychiatric hospitals and are, instead, being received and detained in prison establishments.

In November 1977, Dr. J. H. Orr, the Director of Prison Medical Services, commented on the difficulties and distress felt by the prison service because so many psychiatric patients are finding their way to prison. He went on to say, 'but it was felt that if the prison service was seen to be effectively dealing with the problem, there would be an even greater reluctance on the part of mental hospitals to accept dangerous and possibly disturbed offenders. There was no doubt that mentally ill prisoners should not be in prison, and should be transferred to hospitals; we should not take steps which might cause people outside to conclude that the mentally ill were in their proper place in prison'. Recent publications by the National Schizophrenia Fellowship have drawn attention to this tragic and disgraceful situation. In 'Home Sweet Nothing' (May 1979), for example, the Fellowship proposes, *inter alia*, the development of campus communities comprising a range of sheltered environments, where the changing needs of the patients can be met with minimal disruption, and methods of rehabilitation and criteria of assessment can themselves be properly assessed.

The desperate need for appropriate residential accommodation for mentally disturbed people was also emphasised in the Annual Report, 1976, of the Salvation Army:

> An unfair burden has been placed on such organisations as the Salvation Army who always have large numbers of mentally disturbed men and women sleeping in their hostels. The 1959 Mental Health Act opened the doors of mental hospitals to discharge a stream of patients, who without adequate preparation, were expected to re-enter society and cope with the demands of daily living. ... The vast majority became rootless wanderers, unemployable, frequently charged with criminal offences. Today there are more than seventy thousand people who have been in a mental hospital for a period of two years or more and who have been discharged without adequate provision. ... The Salvation Army does not complain. ... But it does feel most strongly that this great area of social necessity should be examined in depth by the statutory authorities.

The NSF has now started to do just this, and is attracting support in so doing.

An important part in this educational process is increasingly being played by people who themselves have had schizophrenia, who and, with their symptoms controlled by medication, are often back at work and ready to speak of their experiences. Such autobiographical contributions are listened to with great attention because they can detail the sort of help which has been of value at different stages in the illness.

Again, to an increasing extent, National Schizophrenia Fellowship Voluntary Co-ordinators (the name given to those people who put members in touch with each other locally) are being looked to for advice and practical help by all kinds of people, not only other NSF members, in their home district. Residential Study Weekends for Voluntary Co-ordinators are being arranged in order that plenty of time can be given to explore the best sort of guidance that would be helpful to different kinds of enquiries. In this way it is hoped to encourage Voluntary Co-ordinators to have a greater belief in their own ability to help each other – in fact, to help them acquire greater self-confidence in what they are already doing. These Study Weekends, with their follow-up 'refresher day' after three months, promise well and the Fellowship is grateful to the Mental Health Foundation for funding what is still regarded as an experimental project.

The number of local Groups has grown as well as the amount of activity carried out by their members. By January, 1980, the number of Voluntary Co-ordinators had increased to 142. The range of local activities is wide, from the befriending of each other's relatives, to the planning and carrying out of adult education programmes, and to the organisation of local concerts and galas. All these events, carried out in the name of the Fellowship, bring rewarding new contacts in the neighbourhoods where they occur as well as promoting greater understanding among neighbours and friends. Members in one London Borough have arranged an emergency telephone service among themselves, an example which is now being followed in other areas. Yet another NSF Group organise weekly country walks and other outings in which they are joined by member-patients from hospital. A growing number of Fellowship members are invited to speak to groups of social workers, health visitors, general practitioners and to Community Health Councils as well as to various local voluntary organisations. Some members have had the distinction of addressing meetings of the Royal College of Psychiatrists.

Another type of work now being carried out by the Fellowship is the planning and undertaking of national research projects. The appointment of a full-time Research Officer led to a detailed examination of the best way of providing long-term accommodation together with the availability of either occupation or employment. As a result of this study, the Fellowship hopes to provide some kind of residential facilities to help in this most difficult of all fields. Another pioneering task has been carried out by a full-time Adviser/Co-ordinator who worked for two years in order to oil the wheels of communication between the different kinds of professional worker and families in need. The resulting Report, 'Tied Together with String', gives an account of the study of the care available for schizophrenics and their relatives. The author's conclusions reflect 'confusion, not only in relatives but in many professional workers also'. It is made clear that the isolated suffering, despair and anxiety of many relatives and patients is not simply the result of psychiatric illness or of living with someone who is suffering the long-term effects of illness – 'The traumatic experience of accepting a diagnosis of schizophrenia is similar to bereavement or loss in the demands it makes on an individual to make painful adjustments to what may seem bearable'. Those who are responsible for providing health and social services find this report of great interest. 'Relatives who sincerely feel that a patient is not getting the right treatment ... often dare not take action for fear of recrimination damaging future prospects. Their fear is often legitimate'.

The National Schizophrenia Fellowship, which is a Registered Charity, is run by a Council of Management composed of twelve elected members and four Honorary Officers. Finances are always a difficulty. Members are gradually discovering ways of raising funds and support has been given by some helpful and generous Trusts. In addition the Fellowship receives a substantial grant from the Department of Health and Social Security.

Information about the work of the National Schizophrenia Fellowship has spread to other countries particularly in respect of its various publications, two of which have been translated into German, and a Dutch translation is imminent. There are now national Schizophrenia Organisations in New Zealand and in Australia, both due to the efforts of members of the National Schizophrenia Fellowship. The Fellowship is in close touch with members elsewhere who are trying to bring about the foundation of a Schizophrenia Fellowship in their own part of the world.

The word 'research' is always an emotive one when the great disabling diseases are being considered. Research into the cause, or causes, of this or that disease is a steady fund-raising motif – and not less so in this field than in others. But while the Fellowship takes no part in controversies which rage from time to time about the nature of schizophrenia and its treatment, or lack of it, members have been particularly helpful in donating funds earmarked for the research into the causes of schizophrenia which is being undertaken by the Medical Research Council Neurochemical Pharmacological Unit in Cambridge. There a study is being made of post-mortem brain tissue from people who have had schizophrenia. The provisional results of this attempt to identify physical factors in the causation of schizophrenia are of promise and interest.

It is an unescapable conclusion that during the last few years there has been a change in the attitude towards schizophrenia, a change that owes a great deal to the work of the National Schizophrenia Fellowship in Britain. So much today is spoken, broadcast, televised and written about schizophrenia – however inaccurately at times – that the world has become aware that it is a major disabling condition which demands concern. With this concern there will arise, it is hoped, a greater preparedness to find solutions to the grave problems caused by this tragic disease.

INDEX